by CONRAD RICHTER

THE SEA OF GRASS (1937)

TACEY CROMWELL (1942)

THE FREE MAN (1943)

ALWAYS YOUNG AND FAIR (1947)

THE TREES (1940), which is continued in

THE FIELDS (1946) and

THE TOWN (1950)

THE LIGHT IN THE FOREST (1953)

a volume of short stories

EARLY AMERICANA (1936)

and a philosophical journey

THE MOUNTAIN ON THE DESERT (1955)

These are BORZOI BOOKS, published by Alfred A. Knopf

THE MOUNTAIN ON THE DESERT

THE MOUNTAIN
ON THE DESERT

A PHILOSOPHICAL JOURNEY

CONRAD RICHTER

ALFRED A. KNOPF: *NEW YORK* 1955

L. C. CATALOG CARD NUMBER: 55-5617

© CONRAD RICHTER, 1955

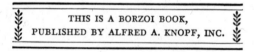

THIS IS A BORZOI BOOK,
PUBLISHED BY ALFRED A. KNOPF, INC.

FIRST EDITION

TO THOSE LIVING AND DEAD

who *at one time or another encouraged me*
to set down this book: "SAINT" (DR. GEORGE
ST. CLAIR) *and* DR. EDWARD F. CASTETTER, *both*
of the University of New Mexico; TOM L.
MASSON; WILLIAM LYON PHELPS; DR. JOSEPH
COLLINS; LEE WILSON DODD; STEWART EDWARD
WHITE; GERALD STANLEY LEE; LUTHER BURBANK
and others.

"If I am not quite right here, I am less wrong than before." THOREAU

FOREWORD

I SHOULD like to tell my readers in advance that this is not another of my novels, but a continuation of the philosophy that underlies them, particularly the trilogy, *The Trees, The Fields,* and *The Town.* In their pages the reader will find passages linking them to *The Mountain on the Desert.* It should be clear, however, that the present book was not written to explain or further develop my novels. It is and was quite the other way around.

Abroad it has not been unusual for a novelist to publish a book of his beliefs in life. American novelists have been slower in this regard. I became aware of Michael's theories in the early 1920's. In 1927 I timidly printed and circulated in private a small paper-bound account of them. The response encouraged Michael to develop his ideas further and me to try to express their sometimes difficult meaning more clearly. I also considered the ambitious undertaking of building up, if possible, a reading public that might in all fairness examine such a work.

It has taken more than twenty-five years to accomplish this hope. In Barrie's seldom read book, *A Window in Thrums,* may be found a character named Jimsy, a printer who spends most of his life composing a single book, setting it up in type, printing and binding it with his own hands, devoting his spare time night and day to his "opus" as it was satirically called, all with little or no chance of popular or monetary return. *The Mountain on the Desert* has been something like that to me. I started it as a young man when first coming on Michael's work, and am still writing it in my sixties. Never could I rest at any age while it remained unwritten. It has been a labor of the inward self with no further expectation than the satisfaction of completing it at last.

CONRAD RICHTER

CONTENTS

THE MOUNTAIN ON THE DESERT

CHAPTER ONE

THE WEAVER

"Escape to the mountain . . ."
GENESIS xix, 17

WE FOUND him on the mountain. There and on the desert nearby we learned to know him. In time we called him our friend and teacher who taught us things unlike we had learned at college. This is an account of the man and some of the things he said. But you must climb the mountain with me to read and understand him.

To get there we leave Albuquerque at five thousand feet above the sea and cross what in Michael's day was the bare mesa. In Tijeras Canyon at less than six thousand feet the junipers begin to grow, both white and red. The Mexicans call them cedro and sabina. There are also piñones, a kind of dwarf pine bearing nuts, and a few alligator-bark junipers known as chinos. When you reach seven thousand feet, you begin to get among the tall pinos, or ponderosa pines, that cover the flanks of the New Mexican mountains up to nine thousand feet.

This is high desert-mountain country. The air is like something you can never drink enough of, the sky a deep blue such as many men who live and die have never seen. The sun shines day after day so that when storms come, you revel in the clouds and rain. They never last very long. By night the stars are likely to be out again, hanging very close to the earth.

Near where the road turns up the mountain is the Mexican village of San Antonito. The words mean in Spanish, Little San Antonio. The other earlier San Antonio, scarcely larger, is three or four miles distant. The high Sandia range hangs over the roofs of both settlements. Twenty-five or thirty years ago when Michael lived in San Antonito, there were (and still are) a few low, flat, adobe houses, a church, a store, a little plaza most always with a cow or a horse in it, and a side street. The side street was where Michael had his house. It was one of the last places you would look for a thinker. But New Mexico is like that. You never know in what obscure canyon or on what sun-baked mesa you will find an artist or scholar in exile. Michael came for the sake of his lungs. The desert cured them and he never went back.

The blue sign on his house read simply, RUG-WEAVER. The sun had faded the letters and he declined to re-paint them. His friends knew where to find him, he said, and too many strangers called now. He needed time to weave, to think, to make the little trips over the New Mexico country he loved. He owned no horse or vehicle, would go on foot or as a guest in some Anglo's car or Mexican leñero's wagon.

The first time I ever saw him was when we took a cabin in the pines not far from San Antonito. I re-member my sensation going to the door and finding this tall, gaunt stranger with a covered, earthenware dish in his hands. He had heard that a member of my family was a health-seeker and had brought a lamb stew. His cast of features interested me. Hairs of a scraggly beard hung on his chin. Would we accept the stew? He had prepared it himself. He spoke humbly, almost like a servant, as if he were the one receiving the favor. He had an accent that once heard was not easily forgotten, but his choice of English words, phrases and construction was excellent. We talked, and he told what the country, the sun, the elevation and mountain air would do for us. Then he left as if he had stayed too long.

That afternoon we all noticed a feeling of well-being. It was the lamb stew, we thought. At the first chance I asked at the store about this man. They said he was just a rug-weaver. However, some fantastic stories were told about him. It was claimed he had been an engineer in a well known Eastern research laboratory. This, Celso Guiterrez, his Mexican neighbor, didn't believe. He said Michael knew nothing about machinery and couldn't even fix a wagon. But he could fix people. He had done something for his brother, Trinidad, in Yrisarri. Nobody knew exactly what, only that Trinidad had been sick a long time and had given goodby to his daughter the last time she came from California. Then one time Michael went along to see him, and after that Trinidad had got pretty good again.

Domingo Sais, who lived by the church, said Michael was a "good man with animals." Once Domingo took him along on the Grant for leña. There was a flock of sheep over the hill from where he stopped t cut wood. Instead of helping with the axe, Michae stayed with the shepherd, helping to patch up a sheep that had been torn by coyotes.

"Not much good for work but he make a good sheep herder," Domingo said.

Another time Michael had gone with him to Albuquerque in the leña truck. Domingo had stopped for gas at the yellow station on the mesa where there was a small zoo. Among the cages was that of a wildcat. It snarled and spat at everyone who came close. But Michael went right up and talked to it. "Like it was people," Domingo said. After a while the wildcat purred like a house cat. He, Domingo, had seen and heard it.

Perhaps the most curious story came from the Mexican boys in San Antonito. They said that one day Felipe Gurule had thrown a stone at a mountain bluebird on a fence post and had hit it the first try. The bird fell to the ground and lay still. Before the boys could run and pick it up, a voice spoke. They looked around and there was big, gaunt Michael. He told them not to touch it. He stood a while doing nothing that they could see. Only his lips moved. After a while the bird flew away.

The boys swore it to be true, but the word of Mexican boys is not very dependable, and nobody but the Mexicans themselves believed it.

Just the same I wondered about our sense of increased health and well-being. A few days later I took Michael's dish back to his house. You had to enter by a blue gate in the wall and go around by the patio, which was simply a large patch of dry earth swept clean. I learned afterward that Mexican children did his house work. There were two doors. One led to his kitchen, the other to his work room. I was to find the latter the most peaceful of rooms. The white New Mexican sun slanted across the floor. There were bright colors and the soft wool of a rug on the loom. A small loft of loose boards hung overhead. The place smelled pleasantly of dry pine and dyes.

Today when I stood at the door, I saw and heard Polito, a school boy from the village, sitting there reading to Michael while he worked. It was a curious, oldtime, almost foreign-village scene, the rug-weaver bent over his loom, nodding gravely at the youth's falterings and mispronouncings as if listening to some wise old counselor. Once he wrote something down in a note book. As I grew to know Michael better I grew inquisitive about that note book. Later on I picked it up. In it I found little or nothing of the books read to him, only strange observations written in English but without much meaning to me at the time.

I remember one of these read, "Distinguishing feature of life, limited energy." On a page farther on I saw a similar phrase, "Basic primal motive, energy hunger."

Now what had this to do with the strange power they credited him with? I wondered.

CHAPTER TWO

MAN'S ENERGY HUNGER

"Energy is endless delight."

BLAKE

MOST OF my friends were skeptical, only a few interested when I told them about the weaver. Three said they would like to get a look at this man who made the wildcat purr.

We agreed to meet at my cabin one Sunday morning. Carl McMinn drove the others out in his car. He had been born in the Philippines, son of a doctor. I knew him to be subject to dark moods and depression. A companion was Dennis Patch, an engineering student. He was afflicted with stammering and I never heard it worse than when he promised to quiz Michael and find out if he ever worked in a research laboratory. The third was a young Muslim Indian, Mohammed. He had enrolled himself at the university as Mohammed Nemo, so as not to take advantage of the famous name of his family.

I could see that Michael was pleased that the three students called on him, and with Mohammed most of all. First, they both knew Asia. Then the Indian was almost childlike in his mild directness. Dennis questioned the weaver on electrochemistry, and I saw his quick and rising respect at the answers. Carl talked to him of those distant parts of the world they both knew. Mohammed kept his simple brown eyes on him.

"They say you're a man of God."

"I think we're all more or less men of God," Michael said. "Some of us just don't realize it till our energy runs low."

"Now I'm sure you are," Mohammed told him. "I feel a brightness in talking to you. The walls and your rug look clearer, as if there's light in them."

"The light looks like it's in the walls and rug but it's in you," Michael said.

Carl's mouth showed disapproval.

"My prof used to say that if anybody sees lights or visions others can't see, he'd better have his head examined."

"Did he say who was to examine our heads?" Michael asked.

"Don't you believe in the experts?"

"Oh, I believe in the good intentions of everybody. I even believe in the experts when they're dealing with matter. Now dealing with man is something else."

"Modern man's discovered a great deal about himself."

"Yes, with the flesh. With matter there's no argument. If it works in the laboratory or the shop, there it is. Most everybody has to admit it. But with mind and its processes, we're a bit out of our depth. Real proof is difficult or impossible. Lacking proof, theories of shock and daring take its place. They stir up our energy and we say these theories have vitality. Their shock-energy brings persuasion, a kind of desperate conviction when proof and fuller judgment are lacking."

"You sound like you don't believe in modern theories about man?"

"I'm just a peasant with mud from the field still on my boots," Michael said. "I've worked so long with my hands that my head's too slow to follow the leader through a lot of hoops. I have to stop and see where I'm at. Also where the leader's at. If his feet aren't standing where he thinks they are, it means he hasn't found the right answers yet. For me, anyway."

"What are the right answers?"

"On what theory?" Michael asked patiently. "They're a good many and they change."

"Some haven't changed so much," Carl said. "For instance, the theory that if you have a bad childhood, it doesn't do you any good."

"He means that adult illness is often caused by suffering or insecurity in childhood," Dennis pointed out.

Michael was silent.

"Well, what do you say?" Carl asked.

"I'd say," Michael answered thoughtfully, "that this is a very acceptable theory to social sciences and the state. All they need do is bring up children by their own approved methods. Then in another generation the whole citizenry will be healthy, normal and perfect."

"It doesn't sound like you think much of it?" Carl said suspiciously.

"If you mean, is it true to a peasant like me, I have to say no. Now understand, even a peasant notices that unpleasant things happen to children and that it leaves some of them afflicted. But the peasant also notices that the afflicted child may have a brother or sister who had the same father and mother and insecure home life. The same unpleasant things happened to him. But often he stays normal and unaffected so far as you can see. He may even have been the one shown less love and affection while the one afflicted may have been the one shown more. The peasant usually has children of his own, often a good many and even the most stupid peasant sees that his children are born different. Some take a hurdle all right while another stumbles and falls. The peasant doesn't know why this is so, but he's resigned because it means the reins are still in the hands of God and not in those of man and the state."

"How do you feel as a scientist?" Dennis asked.

"If you're asking if I'd sooner see it in the hands of God than our own, the answer is yes. If you mean am I uninterested to find out why one child is afflicted and another isn't, my answer is no. I'm very much interested. But my approach is that of an engineer. In the shop when some of the parts break or show faults in the finishing process, we don't assume the finishing process to be the real cause but only the indirect cause. The pieces would break sooner or later anyway unless they could be babied in normal use. I don't see how that could be done, and if it could, it would only lead to a poorer and weaker product."

"Are you hinting that's what's happening to modern man?"

"I'm saying that the physicist and mechanical engineer aren't handicapped like the psychiatrist and social scientist," Michael answered. "One reason man has gone so much farther with material and mechanical things than he has with himself is that he isn't bound by the temporal welfare or pleasure of the material or machine. He can put matter through terrific heat, pressure and many other trials. He can't do that to man. Especially not in a democratic state. An enlightened state has to give man the so-called good things, comforts, convenience, security. To put him under strain and trial is the greatest sin. If we were bound to treat iron with such consideration, we'd still be in the stone age."

We looked at each other.

"You advocate experiment with man?"

"I'd go slow monkeying with man by man. We're too ignorant, and the more intelligent we are, the more chickenhearted, as a rule. Now God and His Powers That Be have no such uneven development—at least not such scruples and shortcomings. They put man and mind through trial and torment, and long before the mechanical age they produced men and minds that we haven't surpassed, probably haven't equaled."

We stirred uneasily.

"You haven't told us yet your reason why suffering makes some children abnormal," Mohammed reminded.

"A shop theory that explains the breakage must also explain why others don't break under the same conditions," Michael pointed out.

"Is there such a theory?"

"There's one," Michael said mildly. "It has the handicap of being my own. It's the energy theory—

understanding man and life by observing the variations in his energy supply and its expenditure. I call it psycho-energics."

We waited.

"Dennis may understand that. I don't," Carl commented.

"It's simple enough," Michael said. "Mind and body are dealt with as the energy-providing plant and spending instrument they are. I don't mean something limited, crude or mechanical but of infinite and sensitive capabilities. A multi-cell organism such as man is capable of registering endless signals. An infinitude of response is made possible by the endless combinations of cell groups, rate-flows and the respective surpluses and deficits involved. The maze of energy paths is without number. Their possibilities are inexhaustible. If ever I use the term 'mechanism,' it doesn't follow that it's purely mechanical. By mechanism I mean that it uses energy, its physical parts, its so-called mental parts, and any possible finer instrument connected with it whose substance and purpose are unknown."

"You mean the spiritual is dependent on energy?"

"If there's a bright angel, it must draw on some kind of energy of its own to empower its delicate and complex mechanism and existence. Otherwise it would go out like a spent candle. This life energy—there may be many forms and wave lengths—is the one ever-present, indispensable factor of life. When it stops, life as we know it stops also."

"I'd say it's the other way round: when life stops, energy stops," Carl put in.

"Life has apparently stopped more than once when energy in the form of first aid or a powerful drug or even the spoken word has set the life processes in motion again," Michael reminded him.

Carl reluctantly admitted that this was so.

"Human energy must be a pretty complicated physiological thing."

"It's extremely complicated although not necessarily physiological."

"But the physiological is the most important?"

"Is it?" Michael pondered. "Coal, boilers, turbines and steam are not necessarily important to what we call electricity. It isn't steam that lights the bulb over your desk. There's some other power there, a good deal quicker, more important and useful. A hydroelectric plant needs neither coal, boilers or steam."

He looked sharply at us and went on.

"It's a little like that with ourselves. Food, drink, medicine have their gradual effect on our strength and well-being. So do gland secretions thrown into the blood stream. But the more sensitive of us know that there's something which through good or bad news can bring strength or extreme weakness on us in a twinkling of an eye. Even the ordinary man reduced almost to impotence by grief may be restored in an instant by the presence of one thought dead or lost. Something else must be operating here, some force more significant and much faster than glands and circulation."

"Bioelectric?" Dennis asked.

"Let's call it simply life energy," Michael said. "I have no laboratory, but I can measure its effect in many ways, and trace its release and expenditure everywhere in life. It leaves, I promise you, a very golden trail."

"What do you mean, golden?" Dennis asked.

"I mean, if there's a desirable substance in the world, it's what we like to call life energy. In youth when the circuits are fresh and resistance at a minimum, mental and physical movement may be effortless and delightful. Sometimes in middle age we can recapture these youth sensations for a moment, and we're amazed at their indescribable lightness and what seems to us pure joy. Even in advanced age when an emergency or unusual combination of circumstances such as approaching death may gather a great concentration of energy, we find it may ride over the corroded circuits and encrustations of experience to reproduce youth sensations with exceptional accuracy. This energy appears to be the chief power with which the commonest as well as the most unusual life phenomena take place."

"What unusual phenomena do you mean?" Carl wanted to know.

"Well, for example, there are authenticated cases of men and women helpless with rheumatism and other afflictions who in the emergency of fire or some other great stimulation of energy have been able to get up, run and are at times cured. Something less dramatic happens to populations during war or siege. You would naturally expect their health to decline. Instead, coincident with the greater release of energy, it frequently improves. We know that actors and preachers live longer than normal lives. We say it's because preachers are exemplary livers. But actors are not. There must be some other cause operating here. I suspect it may be the dramatic preaching and acting which stir up energy flow and flood the circuits, cleaning out corrosion perhaps but more commonly reaching and supplying energy-deficient parts of the body and nervous system."

Mohammed had been leaning forward intently.

"Is human energy the stuff that miracles are performed with?"

"I'm not familiar with miracles," Michael said humbly. "Also, I wouldn't say that energy was human. Animals release and spend it much like we do. I suspect that our needs are greater than theirs, that we have a more complex expenditure system and probably higher rates. Certainly we seldom have enough energy for our human needs. You might say that most of us consciously or unconsciously hunger for energy night and day."

"Isn't that a pretty unnatural situation?" Carl wondered.

"No, I'd say it's pretty natural in the sense that it's the way we've been created. Our energy lack appears to have been too plainly arranged to be a work of chance. First, we're subject to many natural periodic energy deficiencies. We call these getting tired, needing sleep, having to eat, wanting a change, getting sick, growing old and so on. Then there's a more common energy deficiency that comes from releasing energy to relieve local energy shortages. This I won't go into now except to say that it goes on continuously night and day. This persistent energy lack looks like design.

Certainly if we compute the energy of one average star, multiply it by the trillions of stars, we must be convinced that neither the Creator nor the universe has a shortage of energy."

We were silent a while.

"Can't these energy deficiencies of ours be fixed up?" Carl asked.

"Fixing them up, as you call it, or trying to is one of the chief functions of our lives," Michael said thoughtfully. "There are two common methods. One you know. It's repairing the body physiologically so that as a living plant with proper amounts of oxygen, carbohydrates, minerals and other elements, it turns out more energy or lowers the resistance of the circuits, which amounts to the same thing. Physiological bottlenecks in production due to lowered capacity are reopened and restored. This is the physical health approach. It's a big field, but not a fraction of the other which is the field I call psycho-energics."

"Is psycho-energics hard to understand?"

Michael smiled.

"If it is, your bodies and minds don't know it. They've been using psycho-energic processes to supply you with energy all your lives. And your animal friends before you. Man isn't made with free energy always provided. He has to release it."

"I think I get energy from other people," Mohammed said. "I've noticed it especially when I'm tired or discouraged. I have no energy to do much of anything. Then a good friend comes. He gives me new life and energy right away. It acts very quick like you say."

Michael looked on Mohammed gently.

"I'm afraid what you're talking about is suggestive or directive energy. Like other signals and stimuli, it often comes from outside, but what it does as a rule is to arouse, release, nurse and manage your own energy. For instance, there are authentic cases of outside mental influence on another's energy and health, such as between mother and child, patient and practitioner. This influence appears at times to be surprisingly strong and helpful. More obvious forms of directive outside energy are counsel, admonition, example, inspiration and many other things we won't go into here. Of course, raw energy or its ingredients are actually and regularly transferred from the outside as in the case of food, drink or blood transfusion, but these are not the finished product."

"Some believe they get their energy direct from God," Mohammed said.

"Inasmuch as everything created comes from its creator, this is primarily true," Michael agreed. "But it's only begging the question. Many also believe that life energy can be pumped into us mentally from stronger beings, natural or supernatural, by exercise of the will, wish or prayer. I hope this is true and should be the last to deny something I know nothing about. But there must be difficulties involved as in the problem of transferring large and constant amounts of electric power from one plant to another at a distance without the benefit of connecting power lines. I think that much of the misunderstanding here rises from a confusion between signals and power. Signals are transferred, yes, as in the case of your radio, and they are a form of power, but the considerable energy that may result in you from hearing good or alarming news over the radio was not transferred. There's a very great field here, much of it hidden in obscurity, and I shan't attempt to disclose what I don't know. I only know that for the most part and under ordinary circumstances we don't get our energy from another, and indeed there's little need of it."

"If I don't get energy outside myself, where do I get it?" Mohammed demanded.

"You get it from yourself," Michael said simply. "Even in many cases that look supernormal, your energy may be released from your own complex resources."

We looked mystified. Michael smiled.

"Would you like to take me for a little ride?" he asked.

The sun was high and mildly warm when we got into our cars. Michael suggested that we drive down through the Grant. We crossed the cattle guard. There was at that time only a narrow dirt road winding among the cedars. Not far from Golden, Michael had us turn on a second road where we finally came upon rough mine buildings. Today was Sunday and the place deserted.

When we stepped out, Michael reached down to the ground at the side of the road and ran the soft earth through his fingers.

"There's gold in this dirt," he said. "Six or eight dollars to the ton. In fact you've been driving over gold the last four or five miles. There's twenty or thirty square miles of it with gold in every cubic foot. This was the first Anglo gold strike west of the Mississippi. Millions of dollars are still in the ground."

"Why don't they get it out?"

"The gold runs pretty low to the ton," Michael explained. "The only profitable method is washing it out, and you know this is dry country."

Dennis looked across the cedar hills to the dark high range of mountains west of us.

"There's water in the Sandias."

"They tried that. They went up to Las Huertas creek, well over eight thousand feet. They built a wooden flume across these hills, but the engineers hadn't calculated the terrific pressure. When they turned it on, the flume was torn to pieces. In the end they found it difficult and costly to get water from outside. They could, but it didn't pay. The only profitable way was to get it from their own property—from a well they believe taps an underground basin. The well's resources are limited and they have to go to the trouble of pumping the water. So they never have enough to wash out all the gold they'd like to. But so far they've managed to get along."

We peered through the dusty windows, glimpsed the well curb and pump inside. Michael went on.

"It's something like that with our own life mechanism. It's had to learn to get the bulk of its energy from itself. Over thousands of generations, animals and men have developed processes to release their own energy. I call them R processes. Many of these are instinctive, handed down in the egg. Some are learned. You know a good many of these release processes by other names. You use them all the time but I'm not sure you always realize what you're doing."

He took us on a walk about the property. We scratched for nuggets in the arroyos, finding nothing but a few very fine and shining flakes. When we came back to the cars, Dennis spoke.

"You've made me curious about energy-release processes. Will you tell us something about them?"

"It's a pretty big subject to get started on today," Michael said. "I have to go to Galisteo after dinner. But if you come out some other Sunday and if you're really interested, I'll try to tell you about them."

CHAPTER THREE

ENERGY RELEASE IN A CHILD

"In youth before I lost any of my senses, I can remember that I was alive and inhabited my body with inexpressible satisfaction; both its weariness and refreshment were sweet to me."

THOREAU

AFTER LEAVING Michael off at his house, the rest of us had a long talk at mine. Carl summed up the verdict.

"I'm not sure I understand what he means. Just the same I'd like to hear more about this released-energy business."

"He confuses me," Dennis admitted. "But there's something strange—I think I stammered less today than for a long time."

"I was wondering if you noticed it," Carl said. "How about you, Mohammed?"

"Michael knows about God," Mohammed answered. "But all he talks about is man."

We had hoped to meet the following Sunday. It turned out that we couldn't make it for two weeks. We drove down to Michael's house together. Michael looked up with keen pleasure when he saw the three students had come back.

We talked on many things, on weaving, on the

natives, the Penitentes and the fabulous New Mexican country.

"You said you'd tell us about our energy-release processes," Carl said to him.

"Ah, yes!" The weaver sighed as if reminded of a pressing debt. "I've never talked psycho-energics to anybody, only set down notes for myself. Can I make myself clear? Where would I start?"

"Start with us," Carl suggested.

"Well," he nodded. "I guess that's as good a place as any." He looked around at us. "Do you remember anything from two weeks ago? I said that we lived in an energy-limited world with many kinds of personal energy deficiencies. To supply these deficiencies, the organism must release energy from itself."

"I think that's what confused me," Dennis said. "How can I supply energy to myself if I have an energy deficiency?"

"We must remember that the organism isn't a simple entity," Michael explained. "Think of it as a world of cells. The energy of a certain cell group may be low. It doesn't follow that the energy reserves of all the cells in the organism are used up. Your reserves are protected by the elaborate system of what I call cell groups and group combinations. In most of us it's very difficult to draw on and exhaust the organism's energy as a unit such as you might discharge the cells of a battery or series of batteries. You may feel exhausted but the bulk of your cell groups are not necessarily exhausted. If energy can be released from unspent groups and transferred to the fatigued groups in the same organism, you feel renewed strength at once."

"How is that done?"

"Through processes of energy expenditure, flow and transfer."

"You say expenditure and energy flow as if they were different," Dennis mentioned. "Aren't they the same thing?"

"No. We might consider expenditure roughly as the consumption rate and volume established by inheritance and experience. Once established, it seems to be set off automatically in its associated cell groups. Thus energy demand may be made on certain groups while the energy supply of these groups is low, as for example when a neighbor comes to us for favors the second or third time in one day, or perhaps only once but while we are very tired from other labors. Or you may weary yourself studying for an examination and then find you must study for a further examination on the same subject. In such cases and thousands like them, energy must be obtained somewhere in the organism for the tired invoked cell groups. We know that nature abhors a vacuum, so the organism draws on and attempts to transfer some energy available in its system according to inheritance and past experience."

"Just how does it get it? That's what I want to know," Dennis persisted.

"It gets it from brother cell groups it activates for their energy content," Michael answered. "This organic device is what we call an R or release process. In reality, thought and physical action are sequences of such release processes built up by instinct and experience, one needy cell group setting off another for

the benefit of its energy flow. On a summer's day perhaps you've been on the mesa in your car watching
a storm over Mount Taylor. In Albuquerque it may
be clear and bright and you have a view of the
performance. Sixty miles away the storm looks no
more than a local thunderhead. As you watch, you
see lightning playing in it. The light flashes on one
side and then on the other. It seems to come from deep
in the lifeless mass. Sometimes it turns on singly like a
pale lamp in a dark room. But many times it runs in a
series of flashes, all connected including distant winkings deep in the other side of the clouds. These seem
to be simultaneous but are really progressive. Also
you may see two or three disconnected flashes or
winkings at the same time."

Michael shifted his lanky position and went on.

"That's the way we'd look if we could see ourselves psycho-energically. Energy release processes
are being touched off all the time and their power
charges appropriated and spent. Often two, three or
more of our cell groups are active simultaneously.
We'd see irregular sequences of sparks and flashes and
also continuous, sustained lights. These latter would be
the wasteful unrelaxed spending groups we'll come to
later."

"If we have more than one cell group giving us
thoughts at one time, how come we're conscious of
only one?" Carl asked.

"Sometimes we're conscious of a second or third in
the back of our minds," Michael reminded us. "For
instance, we may be dimly aware of fatigue or worry
or a pleasure ahead or past, or the realization that

we've forgotten something. But for the most part we're not conscious of simultaneous activity—only of that cell group spending the most energy. The identity of this dominant group changes according to its own varying energy expenditure and that of associated groups. The group that controls the greatest current energy consumption dominates. This group may not stay in power long, but for the moment it stands for consciousness, represents the organism."

"If this is true, how can we ever think of small insignificant things?" Dennis asked.

"What you call small insignificant things may have a higher rate of spending or be momentarily connected with a much greater combination of cells and energy than you suspect," Michael pointed out. "On the other hand, during our idle moments and relaxed periods, there may be no strong rival cell groups active. During the night when all are asleep, a tree toad or cricket may be the strongest voice in the village."

We were silent, trying to follow him.

"I still don't know how energy is released," Carl complained.

"No, we haven't said much about it yet," Michael agreed cheerfully. "I hope to show you a few release processes in action over at Celso's. But first I wanted to give you an inkling so you might recognize a release process when you see one. The energy in such a process isn't turned on by a valve or even an electric switch. An automatic switchboard is a nearer analogy, but it's very inexact. There's no such visible instrument in us. It's as if the psycho-energic laws governing the manipulation of our energy are themselves the automatic switchboard."

He jumped to his feet.

"Now let's go over to Celso's and see if we can find some of these release processes in action."

In his gangling walk he led the way through the patio and a back gate. Telling us what Celso had raised in the field the year before, he took us on a worn path to the adobe house of his neighbor. Portal posts were the smooth trunks of young pines cut from the mountain and peeled. Weather had stained them. The windows and doors were painted blue and the wall of the portal whitewashed.

Inside of one of the two doors we found a kind of small parlor with an iron bed, a corner fireplace, a stocky Mexican, his stout wife and several dark-eyed children who stared at us. A swarthy baby lay in its home-made cuna, hollowed out of the trunk of a tree.

We were introduced to the parents, and the nature of our call explained. After courtesies and pleasantries in the chopped New Mexican mountain Spanish, Michael went to the cuna and spoke to us.

"Here we have a newborn edition of ourselves. Of course, it's really not as newborn and virgin as you think. Among other things, the baby has inherited a good many processes of releasing its own energy. Most of these are with robbery intent."

"With robbery intent?" Carl repeated puzzled.

"I don't think you understood when I explained what I called the R process. A cell group is activated and soon exhausts its own cell energy. This creates an energy deficit. To help out in this crisis, an associated cell group is invoked, so its energy flow may be aroused and partly appropriated. In good health and a calm state of mind, the arousing and robbery is done so instantly and quietly that the organism is unconscious of the excitation or energy involved, but the robbery is there."

"Can you make it plainer?" Mohammed asked.

"Well, we might roughly liken the human organism to a settlement of people all conjoined in the manner of Siamese twins, with blood vessels connected through muscular fibrous tissue. Let's imagine further that when the people in this illustration are at rest and the pressure is quite low, the blood in an individual circulates in himself alone. It's only during action that higher pressure allows it to reach his connected fellows. So when one individual depletes and must replenish his vitality, instead of falling back on the slower method of rest and recovery, he arouses some of his fellows to wake up and move around. This raises their blood pressure and circulation. Now the depleted individual can draw on some of his fellow's blood, steal it and drink it to help out his own needs."

"What a bloodthirsty vampire business!" Dennis exclaimed.

"The human organism, body and mind, engages in this practise all the time," Michael commented mildly. "It's the common psycho-energic method. But it's done under so many different guises that most of us don't know what's going on. We fail to recognize it as a release process. Strictly speaking it's a relief process. The purpose is to arouse energy flow in secondary groups to relieve a shortage in the primary group.

Now can any of you name the chief R process the baby is using to tap its own energy right now?"

We watched for a few moments.

"You mean its kicking?" Carl asked.

"One of the most ancient and common release processes—physical activity," Michael said. "It causes a movement of energy in the organism. This movement of energy is tapped by many groups including often the currently dominating one. In this case the baby isn't merely kicking. It's also moving its arms and squirming. If it was a little older, it would be out of its cuna crawling or walking around. You'd have a bad time trying to keep up with it, but the baby would be having the time of its life enjoying the rich young energy flows it sets off."

"I thought it was the other way round—that energy caused the activity," Carl remonstrated.

"So it's generally believed," Michael said gravely. "It's true that the kind and extent of activity is determined by the available energy. But it's the energy hunger that sets off the release process. This need may be very slight, no more than daylight or boredom. Now boredom is simply our name for a very low energy flow currently available to the higher groups, producing a dull strain, not enough energy for their rate of expenditure. In grown man an endless number of release processes have been established to release energy mentally to make such a small stream of consciousness palatable."

"Stream of consciousness!" Carl echoed disbelievingly.

"Exactly that," Michael nodded. "Man can lie

quietly while he thinks of this and the other. Each memory may set off enough energy to provide his current needs. Whether awake or asleep, this continuous release process evoking and tapping mental groups for their energy content goes on and is often entirely automatic. When awake man calls it the stream of consciousness. But the average small child hasn't such mental resources to draw on in its new physical mechanism and must get its energy mostly by physical release."

Carl still looked doubtful.

"The sick baby doesn't kick," he reminded.

"Not the very sick," Michael agreed. "If the child's available energy has burned so low or is being used up elsewhere by disease, kicking would cost more energy than it would release. On the other hand, a baby with pain will kick and one with fever may keep turning and fretting. It depends principally on where the energy is needed, where it can more easily get energy, and the facilities in the nervous system for processing and transferring such energy. In any case, you can consider this psycho-energic definition of the life impulse—the basic hunger of primary cell groups for more energy and their consequent incitement of secondary groups to spend energy so the primary groups can get hold of some of it."

We were silent. Michael continued.

"Now what other release process is the baby using?"

"It's playing with a gourd."

"It's a rattle. The baby is stirring up small release processes through its sense of hearing. The energy flow tapped by these sounds comes from man's long history of listening for danger. The fawn and baby partridge will hear a noise and freeze to the ground. Our primitive ancestors did much the same. The baby gets a faint echo of that in the sound of the rattle, just enough to arouse the partly dried-up energy remnants of ancient fear. There being no danger now, the effect is a pleasant release of energy to taste and enjoy."

"How about the other senses?" Dennis asked.

"The sense of a familiar smell reassures a child," Michael said. "By reassures, I mean, it provides energy to relax. A strange smell or feel sets off the painful expending groups of unease or alarm. I once had friends in Schenectady. Their baby always slept with a little knitted blanket. The mother had to wash the blanket sometimes and once it didn't dry in time, so she gave the baby another knitted blanket that looked much like it. The baby felt and sniffed it and threw it away with indignation. I couldn't tell any difference, but the baby could and it cried till it got back the certain smell and feel that represented the energy flows of past experience and security, which released the energy it needed to relax and sleep."

Michael nodded to us and went on.

"This brings us to the fact that a cell group's activity appears to be quieted and relaxed generally by receiving enough energy to relieve its energy deficit. We won't go into it here except to say that it's a basic principle in psycho-energics, and we'll try to get back to it later on."

"You haven't mentioned the sense of sight yet," Carl said.

"No, I kept that till last," Michael confessed. "Psycho-energically, it's the most important of our senses. One reason is its large energy accompaniment through and from ancient man's awareness of danger through the eye, particularly of anything moving. Sight of movement also calls for more energy than stillness because of the constantly changing focus and muscular adjustment required in the observer. Because of these things and the resulting fact that the eye spends more energy than the rest of the senses, sight dominates consciousness as a rule—especially if the thing seen is moving. A mouse crawling across the floor will take your mind off the most important words you may be listening to. Now observe."

Michael took a handkerchief from his pocket and dangled it in front of the child. The baby's activity abruptly ceased. It lay watching the colored handkerchief intently for a few seconds. Then it began to grow restless again. At once Michael started moving the handkerchief back and forward. The child grew still again, watching it.

"Do babies know any other release processes?" Carl asked.

"So far we haven't touched on their favorite. Since you asked for it, Carl, I'd like if you'd set it off. It's really a relief process, but then most release processes are. Are you willing?"

"Why, I guess so," Carl said. "If I can."

"Oh, you can all right," Michael assured him. "All you have to do is pick up the baby." He spoke a few words in explanation to the parents, who grinned broadly.

Carl hesitated. When he saw our looks of amusement, he went ahead and bent over the cuna. The play of the baby suddenly stopped. Its black eyes stared up at this strange apparition of blond hair and blue eyes approaching it.

"The sense of sight with movement dominates," Michael pointed out. "Fear aroused by proximity sets off more energy expenditure than the cells concerned can supply. This makes a vacuum, an energy deficit demanding relief. The next move of the organism is to turn on a release process so some relief energy can be drawn into the vacuum. There's one particular release process that's stood the test of time for delivering energy to children."

Carl's hands fumbled under the baby's arms. For a moment after being lifted, the child stared at his face with quivering lips. Then it started to scream.

"That's the relief process I mean," Michael nodded. "Parents think babies cry because they have pain or are hungry or want to be picked up. Actually pain, hunger and boredom are just our names for certain kinds of energy-flow deficiency. The real reason is psycho-energic. The newborn baby, for instance, isn't hungry and knows nothing about being picked up. It cries to release energy to the deficit caused by the strain and dislocation of being torn from its warm nest and thrust into a strange world."

Carl didn't hear a word Michael said. He stood trying to hold and quiet the screaming, squirming child.

"Can I put the kid back?" he pleaded. Michael lifted the dropped gourd and other things out of the way.

"The need for extra energy must be lessening now." Dennis grinned as the baby's yells subsided.

"Carl's too," Michael said.

"I'm not used to kids," Carl confessed, wiping his face.

We all complimented him. Even the Mexican mother told him through Michael that he had done well.

Only Mohammed had been silent.

"But what does this have to do with God?" he asked plaintively.

Michael sobered.

"More perhaps than you think. What you've just seen is part of the life experience and process of growth. The child was pierced by the arrows of higher expenditure rates which, when combined with their varying states of energy supply or deficit, we call sensation. A psycho-energic record was made and hereafter these rates and sensations can recur for the benefit of memory and release process sequences."

"What's the benefit?" Carl asked.

"One benefit is that these sensations of pain and harmony become the basis of thought and judgment. A bad feeling or unsatisfactory thought is one with a deficiency of energy in the active cell group in question, perhaps a greater expenditure than can be currently supplied. We call this psycho-energic strain names like worry, fear, pain, trouble, dislike, dissatisfaction, or disappointment, depending on the cell groups involved, the rates of expenditure, and the degree of energy deficit."

"Then what's goodness?" Dennis inquired.

"A good thought or feeling is the sensation produced by an activated cell group with enough energy to supply the expenditure required without strain. For example, you've observed that if you're well and abounding in energy, much of your thinking and sensations, even in contact with real obstacles, tends to be good. On the other hand, if you're low in energy, perhaps ill, even common things like music and talk that you enjoy normally may seem painful and bad to you."

"You mean," Carl asked skeptically, "that all the good and bad of life are simply supplied and unsupplied cell group energy?"

"You've greatly oversimplified it, but let it stand," Michael said. "It's why the character and morals of a people living a lush rich life tend to be lower than those of the same people living a harder life. The energy deficits of those living on milk and honey may be more easily supplied and resolved. This enables their organisms to make bad feel good or at least tolerable without the necessity of any change in character or effort to overcome it."

"According to that," Carl disapproved, "if we had enough energy, nothing would be too bad for us. We'd tolerate evil of all kinds."

"What you say is roughly true," Michael answered. "Growth means more tolerance. In growth we retain the high expenditure rates of pain but provide energy facilities to keep them from overcoming us with their horror or excitement. The high expenditure rates of growth still react to evil but growth's energy resources let us recognize and act on evil according to reason and wisdom."

Michael thought for a moment and went on.

"The greater facilities and resources of growth are brought about by two things. One is the larger energy flows established to certain centers by higher rates and volume of expenditure. The other is the establishment and multiplication of energy transfer points. It's not enough merely to have the energy in the organism or to release it. It must be transferred to the deficit groups set off by the badness. But we're getting ahead of ourselves. We better let that go for another day."

CHAPTER FOUR

ENERGY RELEASE IN ADULTS

". . . the silent discharge of energy in the nerves and brain."

WILLA CATHER

WE MADE out to meet at Michael's house in two weeks. When I arrived that Sunday morning, Carl's car already stood outside. Inside I found that Milt Berger, Carl's dark-haired room mate, had come along. Milt had told me the previous week that Carl's black moods seemed less violent lately. He wondered if anything was happening to him. I asked if Carl had spoken about Michael, and Milt said he meant to come and take a look at the weaver for himself.

"I didn't know what I was getting into when you started this," Michael greeted me when I came in, but I could see that he was pleased.

"What I wish I'd seen was Carl holding that baby," Milt said.

"Not only Carl," Michael commented. "All of us may have been worth observing. We all follow our energy veins like a miner does gold. But man's been in the energy business longer than mining. He's worked out methods the miner never dreamed of."

"He means energy-release processes," Dennis told Milt.

Michael nodded.

"Did you ever notice how when we do something hard, most of us tense in some way? A singer may make a face. A runner or high jumper may clench his hands. A baseball pitcher winds up. What we're really doing is releasing energy flow in an attempt to reinforce or relieve the energy strain of what we've got to do."

"What kind of face did Carl make with the baby?" Milt grinned.

"He stuck out his lip. It's a relief process that probably came down in his family. Or he may have picked it up from seeing somebody do it. People who use this particular facial process have found that when they stick out their lips in such a way, they're better able to relieve disagreeable sights or feelings. What they don't realize is that they're tapping a small perhaps but very real underground vein of aroused energy to lower the unpleasant energy deficit."

"It's news to me," Carl said.

"You probably started doing it when you were a kid. Children early find there's relief energy available in a certain twist of their faces. The energy source may have been established by emotional experience or inheritance. When the need comes, they use it. In time their faces can grow into such an expression. It may account for some of the different looks of families and races."

"What kind of face do I make?" Dennis asked.

"And me?" Mohammed asked.

Michael shook his head.

"There are many kinds of relief processes. They don't have to be facial. Varying occasions set off varying cell group deficits which use different release processes to relieve them. The organism tries to set off relief processes as close as possible psycho-energically to the deficit cell groups to be relieved."

He regarded us to see if we followed him and went on.

"The accessibility of energy or the point of transfer is a determining factor in psycho-energics. I thought we might talk about it today. But since Milt wasn't here the other week, maybe we better look at some more release processes. Adult this time. However, before we can have a relief process, we must have an energy deficit to relieve."

He disappeared into his bedroom. When he came out, he carried a few things in an old flour sack.

"Now if you'll come along, I'll pay a call I'd have to make this afternoon anyway."

He led us up the side street to the village placita. Soon we found he was heading toward the most ancient and dilapidated house on the little square. Rains had washed vertical arroyos into the adobe walls. The roof of the portal showed sky when we stood under it. The weaver knocked on the door and was greeted volubly when it opened. Then we were all let in.

The room we entered was dark and close with obnoxious odors. I saw with regret the door closing on sunshine and fresh air behind us. After a moment our eyes made out what had once been a white metal bed. Propped up in the bed was an apparition, the bony frame of a man nearly all skin and rank uncut hair. He looked very old, like one of the lifeless images of paste and hair seen in remote New Mexican churches.

Michael went up to the side of the bed and greeted him, then introduced us in a body. The ancient sick man insisted on holding out his hand to each of us. It was a cold, dank, fetid hand most of us would rather not have touched. The old man mumbled in Spanish.

"He says he's honored by your visit. His house is yours," Michael translated.

I saw several of my companions turn their faces aside in embarrassment. The sick man droned in a hoarse whisper. Michael went on.

"He says he's a hundred years old. He's not sure of his birthday but he remembers when the Navajosa used to raid the village. He lost a small sister they carried away. He never saw her again. She's probably dead now, he says. You don't live very long among the Navajosa. He's outlived all his family. Also his children except Epifania here who takes care of him."

The talk in mountain Spanish went on interminably, broken only by other natives of the village coming in and slipping silently onto a bench along the wall. They had seen us arrive. It was a social event to them, but to me it was an ordeal. The cavelike dimness of the room, the squalor, the putrid odors that had likely hung in the place for years, the incoherent mumbling of the man in bed and the sight of him like some living mummy raised from the grave affected me with a kind of horror. I felt a great impulse to bolt whenever the door opened.

After a while it was too late. Michael turned the old man over, lifted up his tattered shirt and began dressing the loathsome open sores on his body. It was not a pleasant sight. When it was done, Michael had a talk with him again. Finally he shook hands and we had to follow suit.

None of us said anything until we were perhaps twenty or thirty feet from the house when Carl let out a resounding string of oaths.

Michael looked us over mildly.

"Now you see how some of your brothers live. Science still tries to prolong life. But sometimes it's worse to live than to die."

"Is there no hope for him?" Mohammed begged. "To die, I mean."

He said it so anxiously we had to smile and Milt gave vent to short demoniacal laughter.

"Yes, there's hope," Michael said.

He spoke no more of it till we had reached his house and seated ourselves in the sunny, sweet-smelling workshop.

"Well, what did you see? You saw old Canisteo, of course. But did you see yourselves? Under fire, I mean? If you want to know psycho-energics, you daren't let emotional experience keep you from observing your own energy-release processes. That's when you learn the most. If you were children, it wouldn't be expected. You'd have turned and run out or said you wanted to play. You'd have carried on if you weren't allowed to. But being adult, you had to stay and use energy-release processes to support and control yourselves. Now what processes did you see yourselves using?"

"What processes should we have seen, Michael?" Mohammed asked humbly.

"You might have seen Dennis' pained look. Since

most of our distress groups today were set up by sight and smell, the closer our release processes to the eye and nose, the closer the energy transference or transfusion. Now the eye is part of the face. A pained expression on the face carries energy flows established by previous experiences of pain. So when Dennis made that facial expression, it provided a little energy close enough to be drawn on by deficit groups set off by the distressing things he saw and breathed."

"I didn't notice any relief energy," Dennis said.

"You weren't looking for it. Next time you see or smell something that bothers you, make the experiment. Try a facial expression of pain. The relief offered isn't very large but it should be enough to be detected by a sensitive observer. You understand I'm not advocating it, only want you to observe it."

"How about me?" Mohammed asked.

"Your relief process was in your face, too, Mohammed. It looked stony. You know the old saying, 'He sheds grief like a stone.' Of course the stony face isn't stone at all. It callouses the distressed cell groups with energy flow released by the stony look and this reduces the strain. The more it can relieve and silence the distressed cell groups, the less energy is spent because of the offending sight. So a stony face seems to endure by providing an energy flow that more or less disarms the sense signals."

"I don't like that I'm stony faced," Mohammed said. "I'd sooner show sympathy."

"My face sometimes gets stony too," Michael assured him. "It's one of our racial release processes."

"How about Milt?" Carl inquired.

Michael smiled.

"I think we can say that Milt fidgeted. Fidgeting belongs to the physical action process we watched in Celso's baby. Moving around, we know, releases energy. But it releases it to the physical organism as a whole rather than directly to the needy groups instigating the movements. The needy groups get only what they can. However, physical exercise is still one of the best therapeutic release processes to most of us, even though it's of a very primitive order."

"You mean Milt's of a primitive order?" Carl asked with delight.

"No, I wouldn't say that. The physical-action release is common to all kinds of mentality. Beasts in cages pace up and down. So do learned scholars with an intellectual problem. Fidgeting and walking aren't the only forms of the physical action release processes."

"What are some others?"

"Well, the prospect or action of fight stirs up strong flows in the happy warrior. They taste sweet to those who are strong enough in energy resources to afford them. There's also flight, sometimes called escape. This is a double release process, physical action plus something else. First it provides energy by releasing it in physical action. Then it saves energy because the action takes the organism out of range of further distress signals."

"I didn't run away, anyhow." Milt grinned. "How about Carl?"

"Before we get to him, Milt, I should mention another method you used to release energy," Michael said. "A very ancient and often honorable process developed mostly by man. Not all of us have inherited enough of this process for our well-being. But in those who have, there's a certain method of releasing energy to high-spending groups which dissolve very quickly, releasing still larger amounts of energy for enjoyment."

"Tell me what I did!" Milt urged.

"You laughed," Michael said. "The inheritance I mean is a sense of humor. The release process is joking and all kinds of comedy."

Milt was greatly interested.

"Tell me more about this release process, Michael."

"Well, you must understand humor as a technique developed at first unconsciously by man. The idea is to dissolve for a moment the serious reality of high spending groups. The more formidable the expending groups you start with, the more energy is made available when the spending is suddenly dissolved. These formidable expending groups may be the circumstances surrounding the person who jokes or hears the joke. Many of us know there's a greater temptation to joke or laugh in serious places where we daren't. The formidable expending groups may be also in hardship where there's no temptation to laugh but where some hardy companion may lighten his own and your misery by joking. For a time it reduces the high spending of the hardship to the lower expenditure of the humor. This releases energy."

Michael considered us and went on.

"Formidable expending groups, also, are often an integral part of the humor itself. I mean the more serious the opening situation, and the graver the face and manner of the jokester, the more energy is aroused to be released. Jokes with the most energy content are often connected with death, funerals, undertakers, cemeteries, sex and such that carry high-expenditure energy flow. When the serious high-spending rates are successfully dissolved by the joker, energy is released in the continuing flows now unconsumed. Since energy flows tend to subside, some of them soon, the more sudden the denouement or payoff line, the greater the surplus energy left unconsumed for a moment, the heartier and more enjoyable the laughter."

We pressed Michael to repeat until we understood him.

"How about me?" Carl asked.

"You also used two release processes that I noticed," Michael said. "Number one was pushing out your lip like two weeks ago. Number two was an ancient process similar to humor and likewise developed by man. I wouldn't say it was as honorable as humor."

"You mean it's dishonorable?" Milt asked with anticipation.

"It's swearing," Michael told Carl. "You know to be damned means to be burned alive in hell fire forever. Forever is a long time, and ordinary dying is pretty mild and desirable beside it. In fact to be damned is about as horrible a torment as the mind ever conceived. Such a fearful thing carries high expenditure and strong energy flows with it. So when you stub your toe or something gets in your way or it rains over the weekend, the disappointment cell groups of your organism get brief energy relief by first consigning the disappointing conditions or objects to burn in hell fire forever and then by stealing some of the aroused energy flows that accompany this very painful but unreal conception."

Carl, on occasions a great swearer, looked sober.

"I want to know more about this."

"Well, foul and shocking words also carry a strong energy flow. That's why they're often used with the word 'damn.' A man angers you. The more shocking names you call him, the stronger the energy flows released, the more energy your anger deficit can draw on for a moment, and the stronger the sense of relief. The name of a god likewise carries power in energy flows, so it's used along with other things in swearing. The more sacred the god, the more energy flow it carries. So the Christian God with the power of damning people in hell fire forever is found more effective than the names of distant and less real gods like Jupiter and Jove."

"Thanks for giving me pointers how to improve my art," Carl grinned.

"Oh, I can tell you a good deal more," Michael promised. "Unfortunately your favorite R process spends more energy than it releases. First it increases your energy-expenditure burden by adding awareness of the shock or displeasure of others who may be within hearing. The swearer may say he doesn't care who hears it, and at the time of high painful deficit he doesn't because the shock and disapproval of others is only another release process to provide him energy. But later on when the primary deficit is past, he may and usually does care. Also, his normal self, which he may be most of the time, generally disapproves of his own cursing. So for the sake of grabbing temporary energy flow to relieve and bathe injured or offending cell groups, the swearer increases his own energy deficits. It means he's worse off psycho-energically after cursing than before."

"What's a fellow going to do? He's got to do something," Carl said plaintively.

"He's got to do something," Michael agreed. "When we say 'don't' without 'do instead' we take away one release process without giving a substitute. To stop a bad habit, which is nearly always an inefficient release process, another and more economically sound release process must be provided, or the organism will provide its own, perhaps still more unwise and improvident ones."

"What do you mean by economically sound release processes?" Carl asked suspiciously.

"I mean self-liquidating processes. They provide enough energy not only for relief of other needy groups but to relax their own activity after their job's done. Non-self-liquidating release processes keep on spending energy unrelaxed. They're like men who when you need help, bankrupt themselves in your behalf and then attach themselves to you and expect support from you for the rest of their lives. In the end they cost you a lot more than the help they gave you. Some day let me point out a few self-liquidating processes."

"What do I do in the meantime?" Carl grinned.

"Go on with your non-liquidating release process. But observe it. Watch the painful primary deficit turn the swearing on. You'll be more nearly ready for economically sound processes when we come to them."

"You don't mind my swearing?"

"I mind, yes. But psycho-energics must be realistic. There are non-liquidating release processes still worse than swearing."

"Good! What are they?"

"Well, let's take one, shock. I don't mean unwitting shock that we'll deal with some other day, but intended and purposeful shock."

"Can you give examples?"

"Yes, participation in sin, perversion, extreme radicalism, harsh dissonances in music and relationships, obscenity and violence in speech and reading matter, in entertainment and human contacts."

"Modern man believes in tasting and experiencing all extremes of life."

"Ancient man, too," Michael commented. "There's nothing new in shock, but the younger generation likes to think so. Shock carries strong energy flows. The sense of well-being from released shock and sin energy is taken as a sign of progress and emancipation. A young man feels he's discovered a new source of pleasure that superstitious older people have a prejudice against. Men who advocate and justify his favorite kind of shock he calls great thinkers ahead of their time."

"It doesn't seem to hurt some of them," Carl muttered.

"If you have a sluggish organism or a powerful constitution or both, extra energy can be strong-armed from frightened and jolted reservoirs for a long time. However, for the really sensitive or high-spending type, shock energy may not keep flowing as long or as rich as wished. It's an inefficient release process and leaves the organism lower in energy resources. The organism must drop a little on the evolutionary scale to get the same effect, insult or degrade itself or some-one else a little harder to stir up flows of the precious energy known as satisfaction or pleasure. In time the normal healthy release processes of the good life have become too weak and tame for the shock-addict. Only the more violent energies of unnatural and unwhole-some release processes satisfy."

"You mean there are all these release processes!" Mohammed murmured.

"There are many, many more," Michael said. "We've only mentioned a few. There's a certain non-liquidating group that resembles cursing. Certain peo-ple might have used them for energy today if they'd been along with us. I mean they'd have complained about Canisteo's house, criticized the dirt, smells and sanitation, blamed Mexicans in general. Expressed com-plaint, criticism and blame are release processes to get relief energy to cell groups made deficient by pain, hurt, discomfort, slight and many other things. You might say that complaints are the weak sister's curses, criticism the cursing of the intellectual and blame the cursing of the self-righteous. Psycho-energically, there's not much difference. In all of these, energy is aroused and fed to deficit groups. The relief is brief. You've got to keep complaining to keep the relief energy coming. Meantime the talking enlarges and deepens the irritation group deficits. In the end the energy lack is worse than before."

"You mean complaining is as bad as cursing?" Mohammed disbelieved.

"Perhaps a little worse. Cursing indicates a certain vitality or voltage we call spirit usually absent in complaining and confiding."

"Psychiatrists tell us it's unhealthy to repress our feelings," Dennis said.

Michael looked thoughtful.

"You should observe and prove for yourself any psycho-energic claims, including my own. Psychiatrists unfortunately have a poor vantage point of observation. A better vantage point would be if they could observe themselves as patients. It's true that the man with a quick temper has energy flow released by the act and by possible shame from it. This may liquidate the deficits that caused it. But the normally expressive man might be over it with less cell group enlargement and chain energy drain if he held in his temper and turned to other activities as his release processes. Of course, the completely repressive type who harbors and broods over slights and irritations might be improved in energy status if he could express himself normally and release some complaint energy to his deficits. Fortunately, for the most of us, self-expression of our energy deficits is profitable only on unusual occasions."

"When would that be?" Milt wanted to know.

"Well, in a crisis when it's essential to declare how we stand on a certain issue. Then we have no other course than to speak out, even if it hurts. We'd add still more painful distress units, including those of self-contempt, if we didn't. Sometime when you're low in energy, contain your criticism or complaint and notice your release energy flow. Later you may wonder what you were ever concerned with enough to complain about, like the husband and wife who after separation can't remember what they quarreled over. In fact making a habit of containing weak expression— not only negative things but small hopes and enthusiasms—builds up a fund or surplus of energy to supply small deficit emergencies and relax them before they hurt."

"That takes effort," Carl grinned. "Criticism and complaining are easy."

"Easy as going downhill," Michael agreed mildly. "That's why self-expression appeals. But if expression of our irritations has any therapeutic value, our weak friends who talk, complain, criticize, confess, describe their symptoms and troubles to anyone who'll listen, should be the happiest and healthiest people in the world."

CHAPTER FIVE

THE MAZE OF ENERGY PATHS

"All men are struggling through paths which in the end lead to me."

THE GITA

It Was a cold spring day when I went to Michael's again. I could smell piñon and cedar woodsmoke in the air as I drove through the village. The faithful four sat in the weaving room about the fogon, the small adobe fireplace.

Michael was talking.

"Today we examine the technique of energy transference. We know that one cell group alarms another to steal some of its energy. This brings us to a very important factor. I mean efficiency in energy transference. There's a great deal of difference between the kinds of transference. Some we might call direct, some indirect."

"I should think efficiency would depend on the nearness between the groups concerned?" Dennis speculated.

"Nearness isn't always a conception of space," Michael reminded him. "Nearness to heaven for instance is said to be a matter of other measurements than the surveyor's. The same in psycho-energics."

"You spoke of direct and indirect transference," Dennis said.

"They are very rough terms," Michael apologized. "It sounds as if we're delivering energy by truck or pipe line. Electric analogies are closer to the psycho-energic processes but they involve terms and conceptions the rest of our friends here won't understand. So we better stick to honest water, as Timon says, that never left man in the mire."

He took us outside, where he squinted over his garden. He found a small patch that looked especially dry. Nodding with satisfaction, he went to his well, which had a curbing of logs, a windlass and a bucket.

"Now imagine me and my property an organism. I'm the brain. The house and garden are my body. That dry spot there is a cell group needing energy. So I activate another cell group that happens to have plenty of life-giving power in reserve."

He lowered the bucket, raised it full and poured the water on the ground by the well. It flowed toward the dry spot but didn't reach it. The New Mexican dust sucked it up quickly.

"You see what I mean? The transference is indirect. The resistance of other needy groups in between soaks up some of the energy. On the other hand, if this ground had been already moist, the water from my bucket would have carried farther. So with our organism. If there's plenty of energy alive in the system, the released energy will reach its objective in greater quantity. If the organism is low in energy, it will get there in less force and mightn't arrive at all. But either way, this kind of irrigation is inefficient. I call it indirect transference."

"What are some other examples of indirect transference?" Carl asked.

"Well, say hysteria, excitement."

When none of us seemed to get the connection, Michael began to act it out, throwing the bucket back in the well with abandon, violently winding up the windlass, dumping the bucket so erratically on the ground that water splashed on most of us. We scattered while Michael tossed the bucket down the well again. His antics amused us.

"This is far from exact," he admitted, puffing a little. "The excitable organism isn't a poor one-well man like me. It starts pumping energy frantically from a lot of its wells at the same time. If these wells have water, the organism is soon flooded with energy, but the rate of expenditure is so high that the energy is consumed as fast as released. Soon it's drawn energy all out of proportion to its need and ability to replace promptly. When the excitement dies down—that is, when the relief spending is over—there's usually a period of harmony known to most excitable people. It's because energy flows subside more slowly than the demand. This provides a state of surplus that more than balances the organism's current needs. But before long, these energy flows dry up further, wiping out the temporary surplus. Because of the strain they may even go so low as to wipe out normal supplies to the vital centers for ordinary existence. We call this exhaustion or illness."

"What are some other indirect release processes?" Mohammed asked.

"Temper, tantrums, phobias, sport, sex, sadism—"

"Sadism?" Carl asked skeptically.

"Sadistic orgies, I should say. When I was a boy, I saw a sadist in action. Now when I look back with knowledge I didn't have then, I suspect he had energy-deficit centers so deep that it took those powerful energy flows released by revolting cruelty and brutality to reach and satisfy them. Once these inner deficit groups were supplied and relaxed, they let the organism lead a normal life until the flows supplying them dried up or other cell group robbery set off those bottomless pits of deficits again and they needed their drink of blood. Of course, their drink wasn't blood but energy. The sight of blood and suffering provided the energy."

"How about a bad temper?" Carl asked.

Michael turned quiet understanding eyes on him.

"Anger and revenge, strangely enough, often belong to the direct group." He sat in thought for a minute. "Let's go over to Celso's again. Perhaps we can see something of this in action."

"Is Carl going to hold the baby?" Milt grinned.

"Not today." Michael hadn't a ghost of a smile on his face. "We'll need an older child to deal with this time. I want to experiment—see if we can observe the direct transference of energy in action. The human organism isn't wholly wasteful. It's worked out some fairly efficient processes. They take place in adults as well as children but we grownups are too self-conscious for a good demonstration."

He observed us speculatively and went on.

"Children are more natural. One afternoon I sat behind a rowful of small children in a movie theater back

East. When only grownups were on the screen, they twisted, stirred, stood, jumped, did all kinds of gymnastics as processes to release energy to their boredom. The moment a child came on the screen, they stopped and were very quiet watching. The screen child, like their own activity, reached and released their own energy."

We crossed the field to Celso's house again. Michael was welcomed as before and the rest of us courteously treated. I couldn't understand what Michael said to the husband and wife in Spanish, but I could see them look at each other. Their faces remained heavy and bland. Only their eyes showed unease toward their small boy.

Michael turned to us.

"This is Pancho. His real name is Pablo. You remember he came in from the corral while we were here before. He understands little English. He hasn't started school yet."

We looked at the boy. He seemed about five years old, very stocky as so many Mexicans are, with black coarse hair and the blackest of eyes, both of which showed his Indian strain.

"I happen to know," Michael told us, "that Pancho's very fond of his baby sister. So I'm going to tell Celso and his wife that I've come for the baby. I'll say I'm taking it away and they won't see it again."

Pancho's beady black eyes never changed while Michael said this in English but when he spoke in Spanish the boy stiffened.

"No!" he shouted as the man went to the cuna, and

when the weaver tried to lift out the baby, the boy fought him like a young wildcat.

"Anger," Michael told us mildly as he fended off Pancho, "is an ancient energy-release process. It's notable for stirring up in a very short time extraordinarily powerful concentrates of energy useful for overcoming an enemy or a physical problem. But that isn't what we're interested in today. What we want to see is how efficient anger is in transferring energy direct to painful cell groups to relieve them. What are these painful groups in Pancho right now?"

"The baby," Milt said.

"Not primarily. The groups representing the baby are made painful only by their connection with the high expenditure conception of taking the baby away. Because of the terrible thing I propose, I am the arch villain. So the cell groups that represent me in Pancho are the deficit-painful ones. He has to relieve them, so he runs at me. You say it's to defend the baby, but that's more subtle than his simple processes. His nervous organism simply wants to hurt me because his cell groups representing me have violent deficit pains. To scratch me, tear me apart, would carry energy relief directly to those painful groups."

Milt nodded doubtfully. Michael went on.

"Take another example without death. The wife of a violent man voluntarily leaves him. In that case, he may try to beat or kill her. He will give various reasons for his act, but the simple explanation is the same as Pancho's. The cell groups of her personality in him are made painfully deficit by the high spending of her deserting him. These he wants to relieve by violence directed upon her because pain in her releases energy direct to the groups representing her in him. Watch!"

He threw the boy away and reached down again as if to take the baby. The boy ran to the kitchen, seized a knife and was back like some small avenger. The youngest of Mexican children are remarkable miniatures of adult people, and he wielded the knife wickedly. His father had to take it away from him.

Michael spoke to us in English.

"Now I'm going to change the identity of his painful deficit groups. Watch how quickly the direction of his energy transfer changes with it. Watch yourself, Carl. I'm going to tell him you're the one who's really getting the baby, that you liked it so well the other week when you held it that you want to take it along to Albuquerque."

Michael spoke to the boy in Spanish. Instantly the hate in his black eyes turned on Carl. He threw himself on him biting and scratching.

"I once saw a kid like him beat his head on the floor when he got mad," Milt said. "Why did he do that?"

"Failing in direct transference of energy, the organisms will try the indirect," Michael answered. "But the direct is the vigorous child's first choice. If he can't take physical vengeance, he still can get some energy relief to his painful deficit groups by bad words, looks and threats. If those deliver too little energy, then screaming or injury to himself provide release processes that transfer energy indirectly to his deficit groups. Screaming and self-injury also hurt and disturb those who have angered him; so they provide a secondary relief process to the deficit cell groups in him representing those persons. But however direct or indirect, all these release processes are immature and unwise."

"What would you do about them?" Carl asked.

"Substitute wiser ones."

"You mean, give the baby what it wants? Tell the boy you don't want the baby?"

"No, those aren't release processes. That's removing the necessity of any. It's tearing down the steps the boy must climb in life. It means psycho-energic stagnation although the naive call it progress and freedom from want. There is, of course, no freedom from trouble in this world, only a choice sometimes between wise and unwise release processes to relieve trouble."

"What's a wiser process for the boy then?"

"To a psycho-energist the threat of sure punishment is historically effective. It's the Creator's choice. If we don't do certain necessary things in life, certain unpleasant effects follow. Examples of such effects about us you might call nature's threats of punishment. Of late, the punishment method has fallen into disrepute as civilization becomes weaker and more sentimental. Barbaric and insensitive people still use threat, although sometimes for perverted ends. Threat's failure and decline in civilization is due mostly to the reluctance or inability of feeble moderns to enforce it. Their threats have no integrity like the Creator's."

"Psychologists condemn punishment," Milt said.

"The learned doctors of several generations ago condemned the common people for taking seaweed against goiter. They said it was ancient and ignorant superstition. Now they know seaweed is rich in iodine, a specific for common goiter."

Michael glanced around at us and went on.

"It's something like that with punishment and threat of punishment. Ancient peoples found these things made the individual willing to do something undesirable. They had various words for it but no psychoenergic conception how it worked. Actually the threat stirs up energy which, transferred to cell groups of the undesired act, makes them less painful and rebellious, provides the power heretofore lacking to perform the undesired. So the child without energy normally provided to cell groups required in practising the piano finds energy for the act provided by threat of sure and actual punishment. Contemplation of the very painful releases energy for the less painful."

"Punishment has its faults, too," Carl grumbled darkly.

"Agreed," Michael said. "I'm going to threaten Panchito with a beating if he doesn't behave."

He turned and spoke in Spanish to the boy, who glanced back but kept on struggling. Michael spoke to us.

"Threat of punishment is effective only if experience has established painful high deficit groups associated with the punishment in question. Otherwise, there's no energy available there to transfer. A dog may threaten punishment to a child if it pulls his tail, but if the child has no painful experience with a growl, it isn't effective. Something like that happened now. I've never punished or even threatened Panchito before. Even so, he doesn't believe his father would let him be punished. There's not enough pain-energy established in him to be transferred to relax his anger groups."

Michael spoke to Celso, who spoke sharply to the boy. The latter was somewhat affected but he didn't stop his angry struggling.

"Celso is ordering Panchito to be quiet and good," Michael translated. "If he doesn't, he says he'll punish him. But Mexicans don't believe in punishing their children. It's one of the reasons why a Mexican has more dignity in your house than you may have. Maybe it's also one of the reasons why some of them are undisciplined when crossed. Anyway, Panchito has no punishment groups established by his father, and as a result there's little or no pain-energy established to tap."

He spoke to the Mexican father, who hesitated, looked at his wife for advice, then went out to the corral. When he came back he had a stout stick in his hand. This time when he spoke sharply, Panchito subsided.

"Now we have a threat that provides energy to relax Panchito's temper," Michael said. "There's energy connected with the stick. He may have seen another boy beat a dog with a club. It's like showing a gibbet or electric chair to the man who wants to commit murder. Horror releases and transfers enough energy to illicit desire to relax it."

"How about promising a reward instead of threatening punishment?" Dennis asked.

"Promise of reward carries much the same energy

transfer as threat, but from surplus cell groups instead of deficit, from thought of good instead of bad. In the leanness of the old days, it was a fine thing. A small reward carried energy largess to most of us who could well use it. Today we Americans are spoiled by such a higher standard of living that the promise of reward carries much less comparative energy unless the gift is so lavish as to make its frequent use impractical. As such, it's a bribe instead of a reward and tends to corrupt both persons involved."

"Are there any other direct release processes like threat?"

"I suppose there are many, if I made a list of them. One historic example is hate and abhorrence for the enemy in time of war. These furnish energy to overcome a man's dislike of going into the army and the danger of being wounded or killed. I don't personally like such release processes. But the generals must have something or their men will have no morale or fighting power. Man's never been too punctilious in his psycho-energic processes. His purpose has been to find things that control his fellow man's lawlessness or unwillingness to do what's good for him or the state. Now civilization is abandoning some of these ancient processes for more humane but so far less effective ones."

"It's progress, isn't it?"

"It's paper progress. It must work to be actual progress. Another oldtime release process now abandoned is letting the public see the diseased, maimed and mentally disturbed. Once they were to be found on the street. We winced to meet them but energy flows from that wincing were made available to our own sense of health and we were grateful for what well-being we had. It was also a warning, a threat of punishment if we didn't take proper care of ourselves. Now these people are generally shut up in their own pits of wretchedness. The reformers say it's for their good and for ours, because the sight calloused us. I'm afraid the real reason the reformers put them there was the same reason they take their dead today out of their homes to a mortuary. It saves them the pain of seeing the object of unpleasantness at close range. It's a form of escape. Instead of running away, the source of painful signals is taken away. Psycho-energically, it's shortsighted relief. In the case of the physically and mentally maimed, we lose the energy benefits of strong release processes, and our victims lose freedom, which they love so much that some of them try to escape to it."

"That sounds like a defense of pessimism to me," Milt said.

"Pessimism has its good points. It would go pretty hard for some men to die without despair which releases energy to make the high expenditure rates of contemplating oncoming death less painful. Pessimism is one of our release processes. Thinking of the bad releases energy to bathe the good. Of course, you need a strong core to release energy from. Abraham Lincoln had such a core. You remember his favorite poem, 'Oh, why should the spirit of mortal be proud? From the gilded salon to the bier and the shroud.' Read it and see how pessimistic it is. Now, if one's core is weak, the organism must devote itself to optimism for well-being and survival. So the pessimist is the stronger character, the optimist the weaker."

Michael grinned, and we weren't sure if he was having fun with us. Before we could find out, he shook hands with Celso and his wife, made his adieus, and we left.

"Is there any other example of direct transference of energy?" Carl asked when we got back to the weaving room.

"Your swearing," Michael said, still in excellent humor. "Not when you swear at the universe or at life. Then the energy is dissipated over too wide an area. On the other hand, if you know what actually hurt you and curse it by name, you're able to reach the pain group."

"You mean you admit that cursing actually accomplishes something?"

"Look at it," Michael suggested. "First the swearer usually mouths the shocking curse word or words. Then he tries to connect with the painful deficit group in him by naming the article that hurt him. The curse word releases energy flow. Tacking on the name of the offensive person or thing immediately afterward sucks up some of the released energy. The closer you couple the curse with the name of the injured group, the shorter and more direct the transference."

"Will you say that again?" Carl asked.

Michael meekly obliged.

"You can try it out experimentally. Remember, the name of the object that hurt you, if you know it, is the handle of the pain group in yourself. But don't try it here."

"What if the object that hurt me is myself?" Milt asked.

"It usually is," Michael answered. "What an angry person is secretly most angry with is himself for being upset, aroused, made to make an unseemly spectacle of himself. But many people are unwilling consciously to admit self-blame. The primitive organism of such a one hasn't been weaned as yet from primitive release flows. To get energy he blames the outside irritant silently or audibly and so conveys energy to its disturbed group within him, while to the larger irritant, his own weakness and error, he furnishes energy by a whole bag of self-defense tricks. Some day we'll look into that bag."

"I see that swearing should be done with intelligence." Carl grinned.

Michael didn't say anything. He was listening to the sounds of a dogfight that had broken out in the street. He rose and went outside. A big, ugly black and white dog had jumped on a red Chow mongrel. Michael picked up a stick and pried them apart. The smaller dog dodged behind him while the other stood on the far side growling and snarling between Michael's legs.

"Now that's enough, big dog!" Michael said mildly. "Don't you know that cursing and intimidating and blackguarding are inefficient release processes? What you've got to learn is an efficient release process. The first part is holding your tongue. Start saying nothing. Start right now. Don't say a word, just contain your deficit cell groups."

To our amazement the big ugly black and white dog had lessened his growling under Michael's voice. Michael nodded at him with grave approval.

"Yes, it goes hard. Nobody knows it better than I. It's the hardest thing you dogs and we men ever tried to do, keep our mouths shut. Something insults or excites us and our racial self tries to get relief energy flows by way of our mouths. But every word of defense or abuse we say weakens us just that much. No matter what that insulting Chow dog says or how it acts toward you, keep quiet. Once you control and relax your anger, it will release energy to make you purr like a lion."

He reached down and patted the dog.

"Now I can see by your hackles that you're feeling a little better. The thing to do in the meantime is transfer energy to your angry deficit groups by some other release process. Physical action is a good one. How about a little walk? Come on. Down this way. We'll walk to the big arroyo."

Clucking, he started down the road, and the dog trotted along. They made a strange pair, mild-mannered Michael and the savage-looking beast. We stared at each other, half amused, Michael seemed to have forgotten about us. We watched him go far down the clay road, the dog running in the grass at either side. They came back together. Much later when we left the house, the big ugly dog lay quietly in the sun by the house wall. I thought his head had a look almost of dignity as he raised it to watch us go.

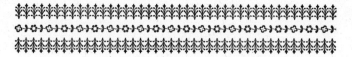

CHAPTER SIX

THE ENERGY CONTENT OF LANGUAGE

"For the ear trieth words as the mouth tasteth meat."
JOB *xxxiv, 3*

I WAS pleased to see a new face at Michael's when next we got together. Carl had brought him. He was a blind graduate student in English, an occasional poet and reciter. Already he had published a number of poems as Carl had magazine pieces.

Like Carl, Mohammed and myself, he was somewhat older than the other students. His friends at school took turns reading aloud to him. He could handle a typewriter perfectly. He had a retentive memory, could repeat whole scenes of Shakespeare's plays by heart, the sonnets by number. My only personal knowledge of him was as a familiar figure on the campus. His name was Robert V. Johnson. Most everyone called him R. V.

"Carl's told me about your energy theories," he said to Michael. "I'm pretty obtuse in these things. I wonder if you could explain them again for my benefit."

"That would be a pretty long story," the weaver answered gravely. "I'm afraid it would bore the others. Is there any part that interests you more than another?"

"I like language," R. V. confessed. "I think you spoke to Carl about certain words having energy."

"All words," Michael told him.

"You mean language as a whole carries energy?"

"As a whole and in part. Language releases energy. The more effective the language, the more effective the energy release. You've noticed that some people find it difficult to stop talking. Even when they don't know what to say next, they'll say, 'and—and.' Some think they just like to talk. It isn't exactly that. Their organisms hunger for the continued energy release from the physical and mental processes of making talk. It often takes a climax, a funny story or brilliant saying of theirs to stop. The climax provides extra energy flow for a few moments. As long as this extra energy lasts, a man doesn't need to keep talking to get it but can take his leave. If he's wise, he'll do it quickly. If he waits until his energy flow subsides, he'll be as bad off as ever."

"You mean such unimportant words like 'and' have energy flow?"

"Oh indeed, although I'd say their main usefulness is as energy-flow directors or controllers. The word 'and' is a suture, taking some of the rate-flow already aroused and transferring it to the rate-flow of the new groups. On the other hand, the word 'Oh!' suddenly interjected is an interrupter. Bearing considerable energy flow of its own established in pain, alarm and such, it's strong enough to relax the sequence of present and recent dominating cell groups, letting the speaker free to go on with some entirely new subject. It also usually transfers some of its own energy to what is to be said, making it more interesting. It's like saying, 'Oh! There's something I forgot to tell you.'"

Michael reflected and went on.

"Now the words 'but,' 'however,' 'at any rate,' 'on the other hand,' and even 'now' the way I've just used it, are only partial or temporary interrupters. The purpose of the speaker in using them is to shut off the past dominating rate-flow for a moment until the next words can establish their own individuality. Once these new words are spoken and dominate consciousness, some of the preceding energy flow is appropriated to make the new idea more vivid or interesting."

"You talk as if language is for the speaker. I thought it was for the hearer," R. V. said.

Michael screwed up his long gaunt face, which I regretted R. V. couldn't see.

"I would say language is self-expression with sometimes the added purpose of communication. The chief purpose is to release energy to the speaker. Even when intended for the listener, words are meant to make him react in certain ways to provide energy relief for the speaker. This energy purpose influences the speaker's choice of words and language. He learns that certain words and combinations of words bring certain energy effects in both himself and others. So he uses words accordingly. Am I saying anything you understand?"

"I'm not sure." The blind man's face was attentive but restrained.

"I mean," the weaver went on, "that the real measure of language is the energy content of words and their arrangement. You know the tone of voice of one speaker may relax you while another may annoy or excite you. The tone is providing you with more energy than expenditure in the one case and less in the other. There are races that speak with a very strong burr like the Scotch and some of the Russians. Anyone who hears them feels the energy required by the speaker to form these words in his mouth. Even though unconscious, there's more physical effort and accomplishment in the speaker than in the words of the soft-spoken races. This effort arouses more energy flow in the speaker and more in the hearer. You mightn't understand him, but you feel the increased energy."

I saw the first gleam in the sightless eyes of the student poet.

"Please go on," he requested.

"Like the voice and tone," the weaver obliged, "so the words a man uses and the way he places them together control energy responses in the speaker and listener. The powerful speaker or writer is an instinctive master of processes to release energy flows in his hearers or readers."

"Are these the same release processes we know?" Carl asked.

"Yes, but in language there are additional processes. One I call merging. A word usually sets off more than one cell group and the energy flow of each are merged. In a brand new word, the merged energy may be thin and slight, say that of the meaning, look and sound of the word and the experience. However, in more common words like 'boy' and 'girl,' each experience with them in person or with the words or pictures representing them, adds a bit more rate-flow. In time when either of these words strikes our eye or ear, it sets off its particular accumulation of merged flows in us. It's like turning a switch so that a circuit of mingled lights, most of them very faint but contributing by weight of numbers, others brighter, flash on at the same time, forming a certain sensory flow from the energy and rates involved."

"How about words that have several different meanings?" R. V. asked.

"Different meanings are often given a word originally to animate it with more energy. For example, the first student or teacher who called a translation of Caesar or Vergil a pony felt the extra vitality of the merged flows when he first thought of it and again when he used the word aloud and students laughed. What gave it the increased energy was the secondary meaning which in this case was the mental conception of the student not having to labor on foot but riding easily on horseback. In the course of the history of a language, a word acquires many new meanings, and most of them are given it for increased energy purposes."

Michael considered, and went on.

"Once a word carries several meanings, then each of them contribute some energy flow when the word is used. For instance, the word 'boy' may suggest a waiter, a servant, a redcap, a child or even a highboy. A word like 'air' may set off the various notions of a wind, a tune, the human spirit, a manner and other things. The particular meaning the speaker intends usually dominates but energy from the subconscious quickening of the other meanings is also present. All of these merge for a moment."

"There are words spelled differently that sound alike," Dennis mentioned.

"Yes, they'd hardly be affected by writing, but they might in speaking. More important, I think, are words with a resemblance in sight or sound to other words and yet with a distinct meaning. When such a word is used, the cell groups of both meanings are invoked and their flows merged. The garden plant 'salvia' may have energy echoes of 'saliva.' Also, a part of a word may have its own individual cell groups which reinforce the rate-flows of the larger group. Such as 'cow' and 'coward.' "

"I've always felt 'coward' an interesting word," R. V. said.

"As a matter of fact," Michael pointed out, "we can never be quick and sensitive enough to detect all the merged energy content of a word. Each word is a chord, sometimes minor, sometimes major, of rate-flows compounded of cell groups established in our experience."

"You begin to excite me," R. V. said.

"Up to this time," Michael went on, "much of our merging has been more or less unconscious. Now let's look at the conscious merging of energy flows. For example, the word 'man' sets off its own certain compound of rate-flows. If you add the word 'big' and say it was 'a big man,' you set off a secondary compound. As one word closely follows and involves the other, the rate-flow of 'big' is merged with that of 'man.' Now if you add the word 'dangerous,' you reinforce the energy flow of 'big man' with the considerably more energy associated with 'danger,' making it stronger and more vivid. How about giving me other examples, well known ones in poetry or something like that?"

It took us a little time to get on the right track.

" 'Wee sleekit, cow'rin', tim'rous beastie,' from Burns," R. V. suggested.

"Good!" Michael beamed.

" 'So red the rose,' from Omar," Mohammed said.

" 'A brotherhood of venerable trees,' from Wordsworth."

"Isn't this just description?" Carl asked.

"Description is one name for reinforcement of rateflow," Michael explained. "But you can describe or reinforce too much. Too many words spread the energy too thinly over each word and as a result the energy effect in us is dulled. There's a point of diminishing returns. We'll get to that later. Right now let's look at different kinds of energy reinforcement. We've had reinforcement with the spoken word. Now let's reinforce with implied or unspoken words. Can anybody tell me what I mean?"

We couldn't. He went on.

"Let's take the same word 'man.' This time instead of calling him a man, let's call him by his occupation, say, 'a tanner.' Now I don't mean the phrase 'this man who's a tanner.' That's too long. It spreads the energy of both meanings, man and tanner, over too many words. When we simply call him 'the tanner' we first imply a man, touching off the energy of this conception, then reinforce it with energy flows from our experience with hides, vats, bark, leather and so on. We've doubled the released energy without adding any more words to dilute it. All these several energy flows are joined in one word, making it stronger, brighter. The same thing happens when we refer to a man as a mule driver or a sailor."

We were getting interested now. I think he felt it. He hitched forward.

"The inventive hunger of man for more energy flow from his words didn't stop there. He found out a long time ago that if instead of saying 'sailor' or 'mule driver' he called them something like a 'tar' or 'mule skinner,' he could give his words still more energy so he and the hearer could feel them more keenly. What happened was that there was now energy from three general cell groups, those of the man, sailor and tar, all merged and concentrated in one word, giving it power."

"How about personal nicknames?" asked Milt, who was never slow.

Michael nodded his quick approval.

"Here we have man again striving for more energy in his speech. Call a man Skinny, and the flow he sets off in you is reinforced by those of leanness, skin and so on. If he's big and you call him Shorty, it adds the flows of bigness and shortness. If he once stole a sheep and you call him Sheep, the energy flows he invokes in you are reinforced by those of a sheep plus the act and consequences of stealing it."

"You mean slang has a scientific basis?" Mohammed asked.

"The slangy and purist are after the same end—increased energy power in their speech," Michael assured. "They use the same psycho-energic processes basically but with different sensitivity and inhibitions. For instance, before slang, man was more of an artist and reinforced his words with energy flow from poetic conceptions. He called a pedestrian a foot traveler and a boat a wave traveler. To the modest energy flows of tramping he merged those of feet and traveling—to those of a boat, those of waves and traveling. Can you give me any more?"

We thought a while.

" 'Watcher of the skies' for astronomer," R. V. suggested.

" 'The fruit of the lips' for speech, from the Bible," this from Milt.

" 'Harvester of the sea' for fisherman," R. V. said again.

" 'He who walks alone' for a leper," Mohammed suggested.

" 'The bear who walks like a man' for a Russian," Michael gave.

"Aren't these metaphors?" Carl asked.

"Psycho-energically," Michael said, "a metaphor is a descriptive phrase with a secondary meaning whose function is to reinforce the cell group representing the first meaning with additional energy so it can glow more brightly in the mind. All metaphors aren't necessarily poetic or dignified. The expression 'top drawer' is an example. When this is used in connection with an object, the cell group representing the object and the grade of its quality are reinforced by energy flow from the mental vision of a top drawer in a desk or table. How about giving some more energy reinforcements of the type called metaphors?"

" 'Castles in Spain,' " R. V. said.

" 'Burn the candle at both ends,' " this from Milt.

" 'Put the cart before the horse,' " Carl suggested.

" 'Upset the apple cart,' " Dennis said quickly.

"The last three," Michael commented, "are especially effective because they're what I call fantastic or topsyturvy. An unusual situation like that sets off a good deal of new energy flow in the hearer or witness. This secondary flow merged with that of primary idea illuminates it with more energy, makes it more vivid. Any more?"

" 'Born with a silver spoon in his mouth,' " Mohammed said.

"Still fantastic," Michael nodded.

" 'The grapevine route.' "

" 'Give an inch, take a mile.' "

" 'Apple pie order.' "

" 'Father Time.' 'The sands of time.' "

"I hope you're seeing what's happening in you psycho-energically with these metaphors," Michael said. "With Father Time, the energy flow from the picture of an old man with a scythe is merged with that of your ordinary or primary conception of time. In the phrase 'sands of time,' you see the sands running out of an hour glass, and energy flows from that are added and merged to those of ordinary time."

"I can't say that I get much of this consciously," Milt confessed.

"No, the most sensitive of us may not be aware of much," Michael said.

"How about poor metaphors?" R. V. asked.

"A metaphor must have points of energy transference in itself and also with the group it stands for," Michael pointed out. "Otherwise, the energy isn't merged economically. Take the old example, 'The ship of state stood on its feet.' The descriptive words in this sentence don't belong to the same general combination of energy groups in us. A ship has no feet, so there's no common transfer point. This means the energy is eaten up, never merges to reach the primary group and illuminate it. We say it's a mixed metaphor. On the other hand, we may say, 'The ship of state rode the rough seas.' Now 'ship' and 'rough seas' belong to the same combination of cell groups in us. The energy can be merged inside the group where its transfer is efficient."

"I think I see," R. V. murmured.

"The crude speaker tries to force energy between unconnected groups in the hearer's mind," Michael pointed out. "The effective speaker takes advantage of natural transfer points. Somebody awhile ago gave a phrase about trees and brotherhood."

" 'A venerable brotherhood of trees,' " R. V. repeated.

"Good. 'Brotherhood' is in the same general family group as 'venerable.' Brothers may have a venerable father. As a result energy is merged and retained in the sentence. It would be psycho-energically less efficient to say, 'a brotherhood of sawn trees' or 'a brotherhood of profitable trees' or 'a brotherhood of beautiful trees.' The metaphors are mixed or poor. What we mean when we say this is that the groups of the individual words are more or less unconnected in our nervous system and the energy can't be easily merged."

"Can you give us another example?" Milt asked.

"Well, let's take the title of a book, Tolstoi's *War and Peace*. Peace being closely connected with war, the cell groups are strongly and naturally connected. Peace comes out of war, war out of peace, and one is often on the lips during the reign of the other. So 'peace,' a mild word, is directly reinforced and strengthened by energy from the very powerful and violent word 'war.'"

"Doesn't contrast have anything to do with it?"

"By contrast I suppose you mean unlikeness. Off-hand I'd say that effective contrast in words calls for more than unlikeness. You need the transfer of energy from one object to another making the words and phrase more vivid. A common point for this energy transfer is an important psycho-energic requirement. For instance, rabbits are unlike war, but if we said 'War and Rabbits' or 'War and Lambs,' nothing much happens, except to someone primarily interested in rabbits or sheep. There's little connection between the two cell groups involved. There's no place to transfer energy. That's to say, the phrase has little power or contrast."

"You surprise me, Michael," R. V. declared.

"I hope so. The technique of energy transference is important. Its efficiency depends on how direct the energy may be transferred. Take for instance the phrase 'beat back the woods.' It's not so strong a phrase in my opinion as 'beat the woods back.' The strong energy flow of the word 'beat' is passed more directly to the quieter energy group standing for 'woods.' You see and feel the action more vividly. It's much the same with 'Blow the man down.' Energy is merged more directly with 'man' than in 'Blow down the man.' "

"That brings up something," Carl broke in. "What's more effective—the adjective before the noun like we say it in English or after a noun like the Spanish do it?"

"It all depends, I think," Michael reflected. "Order of words is like arrangement of plot in novels. Its chief purpose is to arouse energy flow to bathe and bring to life what is being said and done. These energy flows keep the reader interested in what's going on. Otherwise we might go to sleep. The mystery book gets its effect much the same way. It often sets off a violent deficit cell group at the beginning in the form of an unexplained or unpunished murder. This group goes on spending energy and bathing unimportant, often banal, incidents with that energy until the group is finally relaxed and dismissed by the revealed identity and arrest or death of the murderer. Reveal the murderer at the start or half way through, and you'll have to supply some other form of energy release to keep the reader from laying the book down."

"Tell us more about this!" Carl said.

"On the other hand," Michael went on, "you may hear a long anecdote about someone who isn't named or whose name you didn't catch. The details aren't exciting and you're not much interested. You scarcely listen. On the end you learn it's about a friend of yours or at least someone you know. You ask then if it can be told again. If you had known it was he or she at the beginning, the large cell group in you representing this friend or figure would have been very active supplying energy to the things told about him, making them interesting and vivid."

"You spoke awhile ago about the diminishing energy of too many words of description," R. V. reminded.

"I meant chiefly words that get in the way between energising words and those to be energised. As a rule, they absorb more energy than they contribute. Also most word energy flows subside quickly. If several words are interspersed, by the time you get to the word that should receive energy transfer from the earlier word, the energy flow has trickled off and the effect is lost."

"Then the best language is brief?"

"Not always. I would rather say that ideas have more energy and power if the words representing them are compressed. It's rather hard to do. Poets and cowboys, men who live alone and have lots of time to taste words and think about them, are best at it. They and geniuses. For instance, I remember a phrase from Shakespeare, 'full star.' "

R. V.'s face kindled.

" 'That full star that ushers in the even,' " he quoted. Michael nodded.

"It's a good example we haven't touched on up to now. I mean the energy management process of compression. Given the same amount of energy to spend on two phrases, the fewer words of the shorter will naturally be more energised. Let's examine this phrase, 'full star.' First, the hearer's or reader's energy flows established with full moon are merged with those of the star. But that isn't the main source of the phrase's energy. If the poet had said, 'That bright star with a brilliance like the fullness of the moon,' it would have been the merging of energy alone. By compressing the allusion of twelve words into two, you get a concentration of energy that makes the two words sparkle. This is the psycho-energic process of compression."

"I think I see," R .V. exclaimed. His unseeing eyes were turned on the weaver with an intense deference. "How about another of Shakespeare's phrases, 'dry death'?"

"Excellent. The energy rates and flows of dying on land plus those of implied dying in the water are all compressed into two words."

"How about 'old night' from Milton?" Milt asked.

"A milder example. There's not so much energy to be merged and compressed into two words."

" 'The lark at heaven's gate' from Shakespeare again," R. V. said.

"One of the best. The old master seems to have the highest batting average. A great deal more energy than appears is compressed here—the energies of the bird, its singing in the sky, its flight to the very gate of heaven, which word itself carries a great many energy flows of life and death."

" 'I am alpha and omega, the beginning and the end,' " from Milt.

"Very good," Michael said. "There are nine or ten words. But into those nine or ten are compressed about everything we know—birth and death, life, creation and destruction, and above all, the Powers That Be."

After a moment Michael asked if we would drive him to the San Pedro Mountain. We got out of the cars where the mountain dropped away beneath us.

We stood overlooking a large wasteland laced by dry sandy watercourses.

Michael pointed out points of interest, making no concession to R. V., who seemed to prefer that kind of treatment, standing with the others, his sensitive face alive with feeling as if he perceived something beyond sight.

"You see all those arroyos?" Michael asked. "They're dry or seem to be. But you don't have to dig down far in their stream bed to find water. Underground moisture follows all their twists and turns. It comes from past rains and snows. That's the way with words. You don't see the energy flow, but it's there if you dig underneath. It's established from past emotions and experience."

"What are the best words to use in writing?" Carl asked.

"Well, there's still another source of energy in words and phrases that we haven't touched on as yet. I'm sure the power found in these particular words and phrases has been noticed by the bright men who write English text books, although the psycho-energic causes may have escaped them."

"What kind of words do you mean?" Carl asked.

"R. V. wasn't with us the other day," Michael answered. "Perhaps the rest of you will excuse me for repeating how ancient man detected danger and game by means of his senses, principally sight. As a result, strong energy flows are associated with our senses. Visual energy release, being the strongest, usually dominates conciousness. So, other things being equal, word pictures release more energy in the reader and hearer than words of the other senses."

"Are you by any chance speaking of imagery?" R. V. asked.

"Imagery is your name for the visual energy-release process."

"A lot of Shakespeare's power is supposed to be from imagery," Carl said.

"Well, let's see. How about giving us some examples that release energy through the eye?"

Carl couldn't think of any at the moment, but R. V. could.

" 'Proud-pied April.' "

" 'Like the dyer's hand.' "

" 'Lady, by yonder blessed moon I swear, that tips with silver all these fruit-tree tops.' "

" 'Sit, Jessica. Look how the floor of heaven is thick inlaid with patines of bright gold; there's not the smallest orb which thou behold'st but in his motion like an angel sings.' "

"Excellent," Michael praised. "I think you can see what R. V. and Carl call imagery and what I call words that release energy flow established through the eye. So much for poetry. Let's see if the common man found any energy released by slang or colloquial imagery."

It took a few minutes to understand what he wanted. Then we all contributed.

" 'The double cross.' "

" 'The blue stocking.' 'The blues.' "

" 'A dark horse.' "

" 'A feather in his cap.' "

" 'The lame duck.' "

Michael beamed at us.

"Good enough. Now we come to another phase of the eye process. You remember when we were over at Celso's we found out that if the object seen is moving, it releases more energy than when standing still. Well, it has the same effect in words. I wonder if you literary young gentlemen can give me specimens."

We discussed it awhile.

" 'Winking Mary-buds begin to ope their golden eyes,' from *Cymbeline*," R. V. started us off.

" 'If I take the wings of the morning and dwell in the uttermost parts of the sea,' from the Psalms," this from Milt.

"There's another from Shakespeare. From *Hamlet*," R. V. said. " 'Nor do not saw the air too much with your hand thus.' "

"I know a few from Omar Khayyam," Mohammed mentioned. " 'The moving finger writes' and 'Yon rising moon that looks for us again—how oft hereafter will she wax and wane!' "

"I can think of several from the Bible," Milt said. " 'My cup runneth over,' 'The walls of Jericho came tumbling down,' and 'Flee as a bird to your mountain.' "

"There's more from Shakespeare," R. V. said. "Why, man, he doth bestride the narrow world like a Colossus, and we petty men walk under his huge legs and peep about,' from *Julius Caesar*, and 'Tomorrow and tomorrow and tomorrow creeps in this petty pace from day to day,' from *Macbeth*."

"I can't think of any literary gems," Dennis said, "but I can slang. How about, 'I ran into So and So down town'?"

"Very good," Michael declared. "Notice how much more energy is released by 'ran into' than if you said, 'I happened to meet So and So down town.' 'Ran into' implies collision, accident, complications."

"Oh, I know plenty of those," Milt said. " 'He flew off the handle,' 'He blew his top,' 'He got a big kick out of it,' and 'He kicked like a steer.' "

" 'Like a bat out of hell,' " Carl said. " 'Go fly a kite.' 'Jump in the lake.' "

It went fast after that.

" 'Off his trolley.' "

" 'Fall between two stools.' "

" 'Stars fell on Alabama.' "

" 'Swap horses in the middle of a stream.' "

"Now let's skip it," Michael said, pleased with his own contribution. "Let's try words that release energy through the ear. R. V., how about the bard?"

" 'Hark, hark, the dogs do bark,' " Carl grinned.

"I can't think of too much sound in Shakespeare," R. V. confessed. "Not at the moment, anyway. There's 'I'd rather be a dog and bay the moon,' from *Julius Caesar*, and 'Full of sound and fury signifying nothing,' from *Macbeth*."

"There's plenty in the Bible," Milt said. " 'The morning stars sang together, and all the sons of God shouted for joy.' "

"I read one last night in Scott Fitzgerald," Dennis said. " 'Planets in chime.' "

" 'The bells of St. Mary's,' " this from Carl.

When we came to slang, there were still fewer that we could think of.

" 'Oh, for crying out loud!' "

" 'Before you can say Jack Robinson.' "

Michael shook his head.

"It doesn't look like common man released too much energy through ear-words. How about energy flow from taste and smell words? In poetry or slang, it doesn't matter which."

" 'A very ancient and fish-like smell' I think from *The Tempest*, and 'Something is rotten in the state of Denmark,' from *Hamlet*," R. V. said.

" 'I smell a rat,' " Dennis said.

" 'A land flowing with milk and honey,' " Mohammed said.

" 'Wet your whistle,' " Carl said.

" 'The fathers have eaten sour grapes, and the children's teeth are set on edge,' " Milt said.

" 'All the perfumes of Arabia will not sweeten this little hand,' from *Macbeth*," R. V. suggested.

Michael was plainly pleased.

"Now we come to the last of the senses. Energy released from words of feeling."

" 'A thorn in the flesh,' " Mohammed said.

" 'He that toucheth pitch shall be defiled,' " from Milt.

" 'And then the lover, sighing like a furnace,' from *As You Like It*," R. V. said.

"I think R. V. gave another sample of feeling a little while ago when he said, 'full of sound and fury, signifying nothing,' " Carl said.

Michael nodded.

"Many lines have energy flows from words of more than one sense. How about giving me a few?"

We thought for a while.

" 'Bell, book and candle.' "

"Eye and ear and perhaps feeling from religion," Michael analyzed.

" 'Here's mud in your eye.' "

"Eye, movement and feeling," Michael said.

" 'A bee in his bonnet.' "

"Ear, eye, movement, feeling. That's a good one."

" 'Spitting image.' "

"Eye, taste and feeling."

R. V. had been silent up to now.

"I can give you one from Milton.

   'A thousand fantasies
  Begin to throng into my memory,
   Of calling shapes, and beck'ning shadows dire,
   And airy tongues that syllable men's names
   On sands and shores and desert wildernesses.' "

"Very good," Michael nodded. "Eye, movement, ear, feeling and plenty of them."

"There's a phrase I want to ask you about," Milt said. "It's from *The Lost Chord*. I always thought it a powerful one. 'Death's bright angel.' "

"I think that brings us to a new classification." Michael spoke thoughtfully. "First we had simple unconscious merging of energy flows in one word. After that we had conscious merging and reinforcement by using secondary words and phrases. Then we had step-up of energy flow by compression. Finally we talked about energy released by sense words. Well, now we come to energy reinforcement of lines by shock words and conceptions. 'Death's bright angel' uses such a shock word. The words 'angel' and 'bright' are themselves pretty strong, but when used in connection with such a power-rich word as 'death,' they're bathed in energy to make them fairly glow."

"What if she had said, 'The bright angel of death'?" R. V. asked.

"Reactions in different organisms vary. I think to some of us the phrase would have been less powerful and perhaps more beautiful. The word 'death' coming first carries with it such painfully high and uprooting rates that to me it drains energy from the words 'bright' and 'angel.' If the latter words were to come first, they'd have enough energy of their own to glow of themselves for a moment, and the word 'death' coupled so closely after should make them brighter. At least it does in my nervous system."

We repeated the words to ourselves and agreed with him, all but Mohammed, who said he liked it better the other way.

"Isn't 'death' a deficit word?" Dennis asked.

"It is indeed," Michael agreed. "To most people, especially soft modern people, it's so painful that when it's associated with a contemporary or a friend, we often say, 'He passed on' instead of 'died.' Sailors used to say 'Davy Jones' locker' instead of the painful words 'drowning' or 'burial at sea.' As words become overburdened with high expenditure, most of us try to escape by using less deficit-burdened substitutes. The word 'consumption' became too distressing, so we started saying 'tuberculosis.' Then that became loaded and we tried to disguise it with 't.b.' Now 't.b.' has become distressing itself, so out here some of us don't say 'He has t.b.' but 'he's a cure chaser.' It avoids the deficit rates of 't.b.' and substitutes the sense-motion flows of 'chaser.' "

"I guess that's why we don't say 'graveyard' any more," Carl said. "First we changed it to 'cemetery' and now we're changing that to 'memorial park.' "

"Just the same," Michael pointed out, "despite the pain and distress, deficit words carry strong energy flows. The energy simply doesn't measure up to the greater spending or need. Take the word 'dead.' Its energy flows put it in a lot of popular expressions. 'A dead beat,' 'dead pan' and 'a dead stick landing.' Can you give me any more phrases with shock words?—clean ones, I mean."

It didn't take long for us to catch on.

" 'Blood and iron.' "

" 'The gentle lady and the Moor.' "

" 'The viper in his bosom.' "

" 'Lightning never strikes twice in the same place.' "

" 'Stealing the other fellow's thunder.' "

"How about 'thunder mug'?" Carl grinned.

"I can give you a long one from Addison," R. V. volunteered.

> " 'The soul, secure in her existence, smiles
>   At the drawn dagger and defies its point.
>   The stars shall fade away, the sun himself
>   Grow dim with age, and nature sink in years.
>   But thou shalt flourish in immortal youth,

Unhurt amidst the war of elements,
The wreck of matter and the crush of worlds.' "

Michael looked at him with admiration.

"What would we do without you, R. V.? This technique is the opposite of compression. We might call it enlargement with vigor and power. Let's state the idea of Addison's simply. We might say, 'the soul survives and is eternal.' Compare the effect of that on you with Addison's strong energy flow words—'the drawn dagger,' 'the stars shall fade away,' 'the sun himself grow dim.' What's the rest of it?"

" 'The war of elements, the wreck of matter and the crush of worlds.' "

"Splendid. The energy from these powerful words, phrases and conceptions bathe the lines and us with brilliant light and power. Good poetry is full of energy flows. In fact, ordinary words in great poetry are like dark inert stars lighted by the passing bright stars of energy words."

"I can give you more from Shakespeare on that," R. V. volunteered. " 'Lilies that fester smell far worse than weeds' from the Sonnets. And this line that some think is one of the most beautiful ever written. It's from *Macbeth*. 'There lay Duncan, his silver skin laced with his golden blood.' "

Several of us had comments on that.

"Some words are beautiful that aren't strong or shock words at all," Milt declared. "Say 'morning' and 'home' and 'window.' "

"If a word is beautiful and moving to anyone, there are strong rate-flows attached to the word for the person involved. For instance, 'morning' calls up the strong rates of 'night' which it dissolves. 'Home' is most beautiful to somebody in whom deficits have been aroused by the suggestion of being away from home and family. 'Windows' carry a lot of energy flow among prisoners, the bedridden and housebound who look longingly out of windows. The word also associates the absence of a person or ship at sea looked for. More than that, it implies being shut up by walls. Windows are a break through for the eye and spirit."

For a long time that morning we stood in the sun on San Pedro Mountain, looking down on the network of dry arroyos. Michael talked eloquently. This was only a glimpse, he insisted, of energy in language. Before we started for home he came back again to Tolstoi's title *War and Peace*.

"There's something else in these words. I hope to talk about it later on but I can't resist mentioning it today. I mean something more than that certain contrast which is energy transferred from a strong word to a milder one. The phrase 'Viper in his bosom' has contrast and so does 'The gentle lady and the Moor.' But neither has what I mean. I won't talk more about it today except to say that it's the most important process I know. It's the establishment of strong energy flows which keep on after the painful things that made them have passed. Do you see what I mean? Take Tolstoi's title again. The violent and painful flows of war are released in peace. Take 'the lion will lie down with the lamb.' The violent flows of the lion are released in the lamb. Take 'Out of this nettle, danger, we pluck this flower, safety.' The painful flows of 'nettle' and 'danger' are released by and in safety. This mildness isn't weakness. It has beneath it strong energy flows. It's the psycho-energic method for establishing great power in gentleness and beauty. I hope to tell you more about it some day."

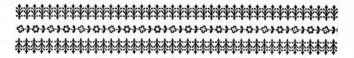

CHAPTER SEVEN

ENERGY RELEASED BY MUSIC
AND BEAUTY

"O, it came o'er my ear like the sweet sound,
That breathes upon a bank of violets,
Stealing and giving odor! Enough; no more:
'Tis not so sweet now as it was before."
TWELFTH NIGHT

WE HAD had snow in New Mexico during the late winter. Down in Albuquerque there was a little, but up above six thousand feet the country on two occasions blinded me with its whiteness. Each time the strong Southwestern sun soon melted it. Spring had come now, and the next Sunday when we went to Michael's place it was very mild. The door stood open. We could hear a phonograph in the village playing *Virgencita, Ventanita Morada* and other Mexican records then popular.

"I suspect," R. V. said, "from the way we play music and listen to it that there's energy in it."

"Music is one of man's R processes," Michael agreed. "It releases energy according to the flows established by our inheritance and experience with music and with life."

"What does life have to do with it?" Carl asked.

"Before that, let's see what musical experience has to

do with it," Michael suggested. "The musician first has an inheritance of R processes which release energy in him to the sound, perhaps even to the sight and environment of music. We say, the child takes to music. Also, practising a musical instrument is an energy-establishing project. It doesn't provide the high rates and strong flows of battle or tragedy, but what it lacks in violence it makes up for in persistence, hour after hour, day after day. Also the effort of mastering difficult music sets up higher rate-flows in the musician. Afterward when he hears other difficult music, it sets off the energy flows founded by his own effort. This effort is unnecessary now, releasing energy for observation and enjoyment."

"How about the common man who likes music?" Carl inquired.

"He may have had an inheritance like although perhaps much smaller than the musician's. Also, the sense of hearing releases energy to all of us including animals. I mean music is a kind of mental energy activity, a continuous stream of energy impulses set off in us as is done by the sounds of a city or a mountain stream. Finally, the layman's experience with music establishes a store of rates and flows connected with it. But most of the layman's reaction to music, and often the composer's too, comes from music's symbolizing of life."

"What do you mean exactly?" Milt asked.

"I mean we can't hear anything without energy rates and flows being set off in us. Life is a continuous sequence of such rates and flows and their effect upon our conscious or unconscious well-being. Now music is a setting off of these same rate-flows of life. They may be unrecognized in us but are there. These symbols of the energy rate-flows of life give music its infinite resources and explain how from only a relatively few notes there can be all the vast literature of music."

"Can you get down to earth and give us some examples?" Carl asked.

"Well, we might start with this instance. I once thought it slight and isolated. A man in New York State told me that when a child in church, he couldn't hear the strong deep, calm of the basses repeating lines in certain hymns without feeling the steady presence of his father, who could always be depended on to come home from work at a certain hour, to bring money for them to live on, to repair the house and his childhood toys, to remain the family's general security against life. I believe now this to be a more general experience than I thought then. The deep steady foundation of the bass fiddles I hear in Mexican tipica orchestras remind me of my childhood admiration for the strength of the men in the village I came from, their deep voices, their constant heavy work in handling horses and carts, in tilling the fields and their defense of the village from men of other villages."

He paused, deliberated and went on.

"If I'd heard a tipica orchestra as a child, I don't think I'd been aware of the resemblance. So I suppose we're unaware of countless life experiences wittingly or unwittingly recorded in music. One such experience we know as a journey. It can be an actual physical journey or more commonly a journey of life impressions. The composer takes us where he wants and shows us what he wills. An original scrambler like

Mozart scorns the beaten path and takes us by a new and unusual route. We think he's bound to set us quickly back on our doorstep like the others do, but he leads us on and on through a labyrinth of new places and feelings and brings us back by some devious and surprising path. Bach, I think, does the same in what he calls *Jesus, Joy of Man's Desiring.* The old German picks us up and carries us on and on round and round and never sets us down at our familiar door till the end, although he comes close to it sometimes."

"Go on, Michael!" we told him.

"But perhaps the most effective factor in music is a phase of life experience that in psycho-energics I call expansion and contraction of energy expenditure. We'll go into it more some other day. It's the most important of our energy processes. No matter how the composer tries, he can't escape producing this process in his hearer, not even if every note and beat are monotonously the same, because disgust or boredom will set in and that's expansion of expenditure in one case and contraction in the other."

"Can you give us an example?" Dennis asked.

"Well, let's take a strong one that nobody could miss: violence or threat of violence, and relief from either one. In major compositions especially you'll find large movements of violence alternated with those of peace and beauty. I think musicians have a name for this combination. What they may not understand is that the violent sounds set off in us high expenditure rates which in turn arouse strong energy flows. Unless we're vigorous enough to supply the energy handily, we don't notice the energy because it's more than consumed by the loud noises. However, when these wane, the energy flows keep on for a while, and now, unconsumed by violence, bathe the softer and more melodic parts of the music with the harmony of surplus energy."

"I always wondered about those loud pounding parts on the piano," R. V. said.

"The expansion and contraction process is repeated endlessly in smaller, less dramatic ways, sometimes in no more than two or three notes," Michael pointed out. "It may be in the changing chords or bass, in the minor, the time. It may be primary or actual as in loudness followed by softness, or fast time followed by slow time. It may be a much subtler reflection of the process from life. I mean a suggestion of major situations like getting hungry followed by food—getting tired followed by rest—being lonely followed by reunion—feeling danger followed by escape or security. I also mean minor situations like the close gloom of a hall or vestibule followed by the airy brightness of the street—the passing in the street of an old bent form followed by a fresh young girl—the sight of gray stone followed by a green leaf—bodily stagnation followed by evacuation. These and a thousand other life examples of the expansion and contraction process are repeated, mimicked, suggested in music. The composer and interpreter wittingly or unwittingly follow the energy veins, drilling, blasting or only searching the rock here, picking up nuggets of released energy there."

"How can we detect the process?" R. V. asked.

"Often it's hidden," Michael said. "You might take

a certain bar or phrase in music especially beautiful to you. Play the individual phrase separately and repeatedly until what preceded it drops away from immediate memory. You'll find many times that the phrase has lost something. Those few notes by themselves are no longer beautiful. What's happened is that the part preceding them was indispensable. It may have been the threat from which you were to be saved, the danger from which you were to escape, the loneliness in which you were to find a friend. The obstruction factor set up the high expenditure which, when dissolved, released the accompanying energy flows to bathe the next few notes with beauty. When you don't have the obstruction to start with, all you have left is ordinary existence without the sense of what you went through to reach it."

Milt said he intended to try the experiment next time he was at a piano. Michael went on.

"The expansion or energy-providing part of the release process may not be in the music at all but be built up in the listener before he hears the music. I mean he may have had expenditure-expanding trouble, a difficult time in his work. Suddenly he hears music. It's a haven that dissolves the painful expenditure for a little and lets him spend the built-up flows on the music, which will sound more beautiful to him now than ordinarily because he has energy available to it."

"You said music was always a reflection of life," Carl said. "How about pure music? I've read that abstract instrumental music was the highest art form because it didn't resemble or symbolize anything."

"In psycho-energics," Michael told him, "there's no

such thing as pure music or abstract art—not any more
than pure language. Unintelligible legal, scientific and
mathematical terms, even foreign words, have their
effect on us. So do words, musical sounds and brush
strokes set down without rhyme or meaning. There
are always the psycho-energic processes. Purposeless
and unmeaning dissonance in the sensitive and low in
energy evokes the inharmonious rate-flows of contra-
diction, conflict, depression and may suggest the tortured mental life of the disturbed, unstrung, psycho-
pathic and insane. But in the insensitive and rich in
energy, especially in youth, it may evoke rather pleasant shock energy. Even I when feeling at my best and
most cheerful may whistle purposely out of tune for
the same playful reason. On the one hand, the pure
mathematical arrangement of notes affects many of us
like meaningless and tiresome geometric patterns, a
boring desert of low energy flows which must be en-
dured and lived through. On the other hand—"

"I agree with you there," Dennis said fervently.

"On the other hand," Michael repeated, "we should
remember there are people who have strong cell
groups, rates and flows established to mathematics, to
inharmonious family life, to industrial noises. The barren waste of the desert that pains and bores many
people has a rich intellectual, emotional and even
spiritual interest for others. But whether boring or interesting, there's no such thing as pure in the sense of
being without meaning or life suggestion to man. If it
reaches his senses, it sets off certain rate-flows established by life experience, if only by his dream life and
forgotten past."

"I'd like to know more about beauty in music," R. V. urged.

Michael got up.

"Beauty's not always in music. How about going out and seeing if we can find it somewhere else?" He looked at us. "Have you any gas? We may have to go a little far. Beauty always takes its price."

When we left, the weaver stowed his long legs under the dashboard of my car and had me lead the way. We drove east on the road past his house, through the gentle rolling cedar and grass lands, past the lone reddish peak of South Mountain and turned north on the Galisteo road. It was only a dirt road then, as was, for that matter, Highway 66 itself.

This was the Estancia Valley, an enormous high trough in still higher country. It stretched more than a score of miles wide, a much greater distance north and south. The Sandia, South and Ortiz Mountains shut it in to the west, the Hills of Pedernal to the east. None of us save Michael had been this way before. We seemed lost in a titanic, unfinished land. The valley floor bulged. Finally we came to a considerable drop like the escarpment that surrounds the Staked Plains. It was apparent now that the valley floor was on several levels and we were on the edge of a top floor looking down into a tremendous basin.

"This is the end of the search," Michael told me and I drove to the side of the road. In my mirror I could see the other car do likewise. Quietly we climbed out.

Confronting us was a broad scene of the Old West with all its immense distances, solitude and magnifi-

cence. The early spring snow had watered the country below. The natural sod that had lain brown and
cured on the stem all winter now had come to life,
and the vast basin was softly green with early grama
grass. On either side, fantastic ridges of colored rock
hemmed it in while far to the north the valley was
dammed up by the great bulk of the Sangre de Cristo
Mountains green with timber and crested with snow.
I have looked on this scene many times since and it
never fails to charm me, but not with the power of
that first impact.

"What a place for a ranch!" Carl exclaimed.

"A Spaniard thought of that several hundred years
ago," Michael told him. "It's been in his family ever
since. About half a million acres."

"I can feel the presence of beauty here," R. V. told
us. He was standing with his face toward the spectacle.

"Not only us but certain animals, too," Michael answered thoughtfully. "My friend Herbert Hardy
used to have a ranch in the Magdalenas. He told me
that when he looked for stray horses he always went
first to the prettiest spots on the ranch. There he was
pretty sure to find them. Now cattle, he said, were indifferent to their surroundings. It's that way with us.
Some of us would see nothing at this place. What are
you stopping for? they'd say. Others are struck
dumb."

"What gives us our sensations here?" Milt asked.

Michael walked along the edge of the escarpment to
an outcropping of white rocks. Here with a few cedars
at our back, we sat in the sun.

"Beauty," he began, "is a cell group, usually a very

large one, activated at a high rate of energy expenditure."

"I thought that was the equation for pain?" Carl interrupted.

"You didn't let me finish. Beauty is a cell group at high expenditure but with energy available to supply the high rate or much of it."

"Where does it get the energy?"

Michael screwed up his face silently a few moments.

"I think we've come to the right spot to answer that. First, you realize we drove here over pretty desolate and barren country. Then suddenly we came in sight of these immense green pastures. The desolate and violent topography set off higher expenditure rates like violence in music. Then suddenly they were resolved by the sight of land flowing in milk and honey, releasing the energy. Energy flows, we know, subside. However, here we keep glancing around at the violent desolate country still surrounding the basin. We look up at the barren hills and ridges where nothing grows. Sight of these uninhabitable places suggests sore feet, thirst, starvation, death; renews the topographical pain rates. Then we look back to the basin again and see it fertile and green, promising water and food, softness under foot and life. The pains are resolved and their energy flows are quickly and deftly caught in us and used."

We followed his words with our eyes.

"The dual process goes on," Michael continued. "Pain rates of intense loneliness and helplessness are stirred up by the inhospitable vastness, by the frightening thought of the long hours or days on foot or horseback required to get anywhere in those hills, by fear impulses from the memory of Indians who not so long ago lurked there. Also those tremendous mountains blocking the valley do something to us. The white snows on their peaks set off the rates of bitter cold, loftiness, hard breath and exertion to climb to the top. Yet instantly the eye can look down into the valley where it's green, mild, summery, soft and idyllic, releasing the aroused energies to bathe and harmonize what we see."

"Then beauty always has pain in it?" R. V. asked quietly.

"I would rather call it high expenditure of energy, usually higher than the supply," Michael said. "It's what provides the energy necessary for the sense of beauty. This high expenditure may be evoked by the object seen or be in the beholder's experience just before or while he looks on it. As a boy I worked very hard on a farm. When I got the chance to sit down for a minute in the barn or field, I thought I saw a most beautiful scene. Later when I came back to it expecting the same picture, I was disappointed to find it quite ordinary. The high energy expenditure necessary for dissolution by rest, so the released energy could be applied to the scene, was lacking."

He thought for a moment and went on.

"There is also a condition when the high energy deficit may not be actually there but sensed by the beholder as imminent. Sometimes the sensitive person experiencing a scene or passage of music of great beauty feels he can't stand any more. It costs him so much energy at such a high rate that to meet it in his present condition he must strain every resource. If still more beauty were to be heaped on, he feels the greater energy required would bankrupt him."

R. V. turned on Michael, his face alive with feeling.

"Millay must have felt that. She was writing of the beauty of the woods in autumn. She wrote, 'let fall no burning leaf; prithee, let no bird call.' "

"It's a price paid by certain organisms for their great energy-spending development," Michael agreed. "We call such persons sensitive because things touch off more in them than in us. An ordinary man may read a paragraph in the morning paper and think nothing of it. The statesman reading the same thing may be excited, alarmed, see international reactions, possible war or peace. The statesman has in him a chain of experience and development that the ordinary man doesn't have. So things that mean little or nothing to most of us may in the sensitive touch off powerful cell groups into action, causing such immediate and vast disbursements of energy that the sensitive's organism is impoverished. If this extravagance is continued from one thing to another, it becomes a case of energy bankruptcy. Such an organism must guard itself religiously against exposure to strong stimuli."

"You mean all sensitives are of high development?"

"I wouldn't say that. Sensitivity is relative. Low energy conditions make for irritability in the unintelligent as in the intelligent. In either case it may be due to overwork, extra responsibility, too much energy expenditure of many kinds. It may also be due to organic causes which reduce the production of energy. We know that an ill person is generally sensitive to noise and excitement because his weakness is unable to supply their ordinary energy demands. But there's always the chance that sensitivity in the individual we meet may be due to greater-than-average spending rates. I mean that the seemingly intelligent or unintelligent person who gets unduly affected may have an inner capacity for energy spending of which we are unaware, and this should never be lost sight of."

"What I can't understand," Dennis said, "is why you say pain must always be present in beauty. Take a beautiful sunset. There's no pain in that."

"No obvious pain perhaps, but a great deal is suggested," Michael pointed out. "I mean that the violent red and orange skies may touch off in us hidden fears and horrors established in primitive man's experience with or from legends of terrible volcanic eruptions, grass and forest fires or from real or fancied punishment by some ruler or by man's evil and horrible tribal gods. High expenditure associated with this color was also established during the Middle Ages by the fear and imaginings of hell fire, and in most ages by the blood of executions. Today some of these high rates and many others may be set off in us by a brilliant sunset. Actual danger not being present at the moment, the high rates are resolved, leaving the unconsumed energy flows to bathe us with what we call beauty."

"If there's pain always present in beauty," Mohammed said, "how can there be anything like a quiet and happy life?"

"If you mean a happy and beautiful life without any obstruction or pain, I'm afraid there isn't any," Michael answered. "The happiness and beauty you see isn't so much in the observed as the observer. The workers in the field who look so peaceful and contented to you are probably sweated, tired, worried over their own problems. You see a flock of pigeons tranquilly circling the village. If you stand on a roof when they fly close overhead, you'll be surprised how their wings toil and strain. The monks and nuns of a benevolent monastery or convent devote a great deal of time daily to imagining and reliving the sufferings of Christ. A village looks calm and peaceful and happy to you because you don't know the secret obstructions, hopes, fears and pain that provide energy flows to make village life endurable to its inhabitants."

"I've talked with men who fled the States and lived happy lives in the Islands," Carl said.

"Ah, refuge," Michael nodded. "It's still the same release process, only the trouble and pain happen before the men came to their haven. Whatever the men fled from, the high rates no longer applied in escape. This freed the pain-energy to bathe the place of refuge with beauty and contentment. But only for so long as those pain-energy flows were kept revived. If death or imprisonment or misery waited for a man back in the States, such knowledge kept the release process alive. On the other hand, should the fugitive be pardoned, the source of happiness in his refuge would be closed, unless in the meantime he'd formed new energy-release processes associated with his refuge."

He nodded at us and went on.

"If you've ever lived in northern New York State and gone South to escape the winter, you've had a good example. First you had the experience of winter before you left. All the time you're South you know winter's still in the North. Your mind and the newspapers keep telling you. Realization of bitter cold up North releases energy flow to your summer weather down South. But once you know that summer's come to the North, the ice and snow sources of your Southern pleasure dry up and you go back."

Mohammed looked unhappy.

"You mean I couldn't go down in this beautiful green valley, build a cottage for myself and be content?"

"Not unless you're fleeing from something. Stagnation or boredom, which are just other words for the drying up of energy flows, would set in."

"What unpleasantness or pain is there in looking at the ocean?" Carl asked. "I never get tired of that, especially when it's in motion."

"Pain in the sea? There's always been a great deal. Most of us feel the ancient danger, mystery and power when we stand beside it. The more violent the sea, the more possible are shipwreck and drowning. In a calm sea, the suggestion is less obvious, but it's still there. Its expenditure has been resolved now by the absence of danger and violence. Of course, there are many other sources of energy release such as the promise of fishing, swimming, boating and foreign lands."

"How about what Wordsworth called 'the soft eye-music of slow moving boughs'?" R. V. asked. "I saw it once or twice before I lost my sight. I think Katherine Mansfield saw it, too. She wrote, 'The sky is full of music. Music comes streaming down the great beams.

The wind touched the harp-like trees, shakes little jets of music.' "

"I think I know what you mean," Michael answered. "There's of course sight and movement energy, but something more than that. I suspect not everyone sees beauty in what you describe and then not every time. Those who do, and when they do, have a sensitivity and energy born of high rates available at the time. For instance, this person you mention. Was she a strong, healthy and happy person?"

"No, she was in the south of France with a sickness that eventually killed her. She felt wretched much of the time. This was one of her happy experiences."

"Ah, yes, you see?" Michael said kindly. "Her ill health and discouragement were possibly the pain mother of the rich energy flows of the hour. There's something else if I saw and felt what you did. The shape and movement of the leaves and branches suggest the living creature of the tree, a kind of arboreal Pan, and there's always a hidden tremor of wild animistic mystery in that."

"I'm beginning to see your processes better, Michael," R. V. said. "I think they make me more satisfied with myself."

"I'm glad," Michael told him. "The energy theory is the only one I know that explains the seeming contradictions of happiness. Sufficient energy released to our current expenditure groups is the heaven within us. It explains why happiness can happen as easily to the man without a shirt as the man with one, perhaps more easily. We see that shirts, cars, houses, money are only symbols, pawns, an illusion. The real cause is the surplus-energy equation. Often when happiness is achieved, it appears to die in the hand. What happens in this case is that energy flow has been produced by the pains of not having something we want. As long as we work and strive for what we want, energy is released by daily acts, partial accomplishment and by looking forward to final accomplishment which for a moment brings mental cessation of high consumption rates with the glow of suddenly released energy flows. But once we actually get what we want, these energy flows decline permanently unless renewed, and happiness declines with them."

"Then you don't think if I'd get my sight back, I'd be happy?"

"For a while," Michael mused. "In time the released energy flows of escape from blindness would pass. Seeing would become natural, ordinary. Other problems, no longer supplied and kept in the background by energy from the greater problem of blindness, would appear, and you'd need new sources of energy for joy."

"Very old people sometimes have peace and contentment," Milt observed.

"Biological absence of draining energy expenditure probably contributes to their energy surplus," Michael said. "Energy flows may also be set off by death, which they see so close ahead. This energy bathes their life while it lasts."

"Then we never really get happiness?"

"Not permanent happiness without renewal—at least not on our energy-limited planet. It would mean stagnation. Also, as we live, we develop a greater range and higher expenditure rates of cell groups which must be supplied with energy when touched off. In other words, what you call happiness becomes each year more complex, requires more energy, more release processes and transfer points. Even the so-called simple happiness of a child is complex enough. When I was a boy in the low lands, I'd think of high mountains and feel happiness at the thought of being there. Mountains and happiness were synonymous. But even then, I know now, my happiness was a sensation woven of many things, escape from the tiresome flat land and existence, a new life among the clear streams, waterfalls, ridges, high meadows and mountain game; the hunters and mountain people; the mountain-flavored names of their surroundings. In other words, my happiness was a combination of many cell groups all contributing their rates and flows, their deficits and surpluses, their release processes and transfer points, to one general sensation."

He paused, looked around at us sagely and went on.

"Today my happiness is still more complex. It's dependent among other things on the happiness, or at least the well-being, of many wretched or unfortunate people I know and many more that I don't know. I couldn't be really content while they were suffering, in distress or committed on fatal roads, nor while animals who feel and suffer as we do are in despair in their slaughter pens. The deficit rates of all their unhappiness or misfortune invoked in me would drain and bankrupt the energy surplus of my happiness."

"Even if this pain is good for them?" R. V. asked.

"I didn't say it was always good for them," Michael

corrected sadly. "Only those powers who can see farther than I know that. What I tried to show was that the pain of higher expenditure of energy is the mother of psycho-energic growth. In most cases I can see it's very good. We would be nothing without it. In other cases, a possible good result is hidden from me. Just the same, even in those cases where the end is undeniably good, the means troubles me. You might say I am the weak one who acknowledges the brilliant engineering of the Creator's process of obstruction and suffering for our benefit, but who holds back painfully from using it on any living thing but himself."

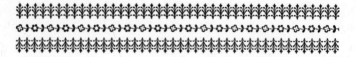

CHAPTER EIGHT

THE ENERGY BASIS OF NEUROSES

"You must hide something, be afraid of something, something tortures you, something lacking, and suddenly; there is nothing to hide, nothing to be afraid of; nothing to be tortured over; nothing to want."

TOLSTOI'S JOURNAL

SOME OF us knew that Milt had been pushing himself. He had taken on a heavy schedule for his master's degree, carrying an assistantship on the side. It meant correcting papers for two or three instructors and also teaching occasionally when one of them fell ill. This Sunday he seemed particularly harassed.

Michael noticed it too.

"Aren't you working too hard, Milt?"

Milt shook his head.

"I've been nervous before without working too hard. If I have to have this thing, I'd sooner have a reason for it than not know what in God's name it was."

Michael looked at him with understanding.

"You should know the basic cause by this time."

"You mean lack of energy. Modern psychiatry doesn't hold to that, Michael. I mean to the theory that nervous exhaustion is caused by the human battery running down. The new theory is that exhaustion's a symptom of anxiety states due to conflict, and if conflict would stop, exhaustion would disappear at once."

Michael heard him patiently.

"Did you find your conflict?"

"Well, we thought so," Milt hedged.

"And your exhaustion and nervousness disappeared?"

"Go on with your psycho-energics, Michael," Milt said. "I shouldn't have interrupted."

"I think," Michael suggested, "that when you said psychiatry, you meant certain schools. Freud didn't originate the idea of a mental or subconscious cause of sickness. He was just the author of a theory or set of theories about it that caught the modern fancy. Since his theories have been accepted and practised, instead of mental ill health getting less, it's grown by leaps and bounds. What success man's had in treating it has not been so much from Freud as from gadgetry, physical methods, drugs, non-Freudian mental methods and shock that reach and relax not only the original deficits of energy-spending groups but the abnormal release processes built up to try to supply them. All of this saves a great deal of energy which further restores the normal processes."

"You don't think much of Freud?"

"I think the appeal of his cause was weighted with what to honest scientists would have been an embarrassment of inducement and seducement.

"What do you mean?"

"Well, first, his followers mistook the presence of shock energy from daring and even revolting theories for the legitimate energy release from successful solution of mental problems. What scientific caution and honest reservations remained were gradually swept away by the grants of largesse and personal power

that most revolutions bring. For instance, Freud's theories gave his disciples intellectual superiority over
their fellows. They went God a step farther. They
didn't merely know and judge a man for what went
on in his conscious mind and secret heart but for the
more terrible indictment of sins in his subconscious
about which he knew nothing but which they in their
new omniscience could detect. Civil jury proof of
their accusations would have been difficult to obtain,
so the practitioner in addition to being God was also
judge, jury, accuser and expert witness. The accused
was encouraged to make full and detailed confession,
but not allowed to speak in his own defense because
he knew nothing about the crime anyway, and most
everything he said only testified to his guilt in the secret code of the expert who did know. It was very
much the totalitarian trial pattern, and the totalitarian
type of mind is readily found in its practise."

Michael sat grave in thought for a moment, then
went on.

"But that wasn't all! The great success of the movement, like that of the totalitarians, offered strong mass
bribery to the honest hold-out psychiatrist. He found
the intellectual public eager to accept suggestive and
descriptive words of symptom states for causes and
explanations in return for doctrinal favors. These favors, desperately wanted by pleasure-loving moderns,
including some in robes and high places, were medical
justification for sexual freedom, discarding of other
standard inhibitions, blaming others for their own ills
and the coddling of their shortcomings from the normal healthy scrutiny and rebuffs of life. Freud once

described himself as an adventurer, and his movement was one of those adventures that caught certain men's imagination. He believed himself a Columbus sailing new seas, but when we estimate the movement from our knowledge of psycho-energics, his career resembles more nearly that of a beautiful and ambitious adventuress in some medieval court of easy virtue. Her worshippers are legion and centuries after she's dead and returned to dust, books are written about her conquests, and coteries devoted to her memory and to the practise of her methods of releasing energy by the intricate and endless manipulation of the sexual theme device."

"What do you mean by the phrase 'suggestive word description of symptom states used as explanations'?" Milt inquired.

Michael considered.

"Before answering that, may I ask you a question? A while ago you used the term 'anxiety state.' What's the Freudian explanation for this term?"

"It's supposed to be some unknown inner conflict near the surface of your unconscious," Milt said. "A kind of dark, mysterious and seemingly evil beast rising like Proteus from the sea and alarming you."

"Well, that's what I mean by a descriptive word picture of a symptom state given as a cause or explanation," Michael told him. "I think you'll agree that it's a very suggestive and formidable picture. We have strong painful energy deficits aroused by visual, movement and danger words. The patient at once feels he understands it and that it's true. The hypochondriac or neurotic always felt there was some such sinister and dangerous thing wrong with him. Now it's medically confirmed. His family, friends and doctor probably grew tired of listening to his symptoms and complaints. Now he has a doctor who not only listens but wants him to talk more about himself, confide and complain by the hour and month. It's a psychoneurotic's windfall. The patient gladly pays any price he can afford. He gets more out of it, at least while it's going on, than the doctor."

"You don't think much of psychoanalysis?"

"You must understand," Michael reminded, "that medicine no less than fashion has gone by fads and fancies. In medieval days in England it was believed that inward trouble was caused by a lizard that slipped through a man's mouth and down into his viscera while he slept. It was very popular pathology because then as now all the patient had to do was get the lizard out of the deep recesses of his being and he would be well. The cure was to go to a well or spring of renown, make your couch beside it and keep your mouth open for long periods in the hope that the lizard would get thirsty and come out to drink. Certain founts had great fame as psychoanalysts have now, and skeptics who spoke against medieval lizard-decoying were as unpopular as those who speak against the modern practise."

"You don't believe in inner conflict?" Milt asked.

"Of course, but not as the great cause of mental illness. Conflict's power as an alleged cause lies in its suggestive and convincing word picture used as an explanation. It suggests two beings in the subconscious fighting each other and wearing the other out. The word 'inner' serves to dismiss it from lay understanding. It's like a magician showing us an object for a moment, declaring what it is and then whisking it out of our sight and investigation. Now it happens that energy isn't spent in the subconscious or conscious in this way and a shop engineer couldn't pass apt descriptions and mythological analogies for technical explanations. The engineer has no sacred office, no secret couch, no immunity from public check of his hits and misses. He knows hard-boiled inspectors are waiting to put his theory through practical tests to see whether or not it actually works and meets requirements."

"How about the claims of immediate recovery when conflict or an anxiety state's removed?" Milt inquired.

"What you're saying is that a disease is better at once when its chief symptom has disappeared. Sometimes this is true, sometimes not. When true, bioelectric energy is quite capable of the quickness of recovery. No other known bodily agent is so quick."

"What do you mean that sometimes it isn't true?"

"Well, let's look at the anxiety state. It's a field of R processes invoked to release energy to strong inner active deficits. As such, it's a symptom, not a cause. Now assume that we can reach with energy and resolve the original deficit that's setting off the release processes which in turn form the symptom field. If the vitality's unimpaired, energy robbed and wasted all along the line is now saved and immediately available. A man feels better instantly. Whatever the mysterious trouble, it's gone. On the other hand, if vitality is im-

paired, a great many long-robbed, disabled and perhaps damaged groups must be gradually relieved and
restored first. This repairing and the rise of energy
flow to levels of well-being may take some time. In
such cases, the real cause is removed and yet for a
time the symptoms will be there. The opposite of what
you claim is true."

"How about the cures?"

"I am skeptical of claims of cures or propaganda
inferring cures put out by or with the silent encouragement of a movement or individuals whose reputa-
tions and influence are enhanced. What our democ-
racy lacks is a careful, independent public poll of
treated patients and responsible members of their
families so that the intelligent and unintelligent ill can
read the summary of results, know where the best results have been obtained and what their own chances
are."

"Is the patient capable of knowing medical results?"
Milt asked.

"That sounds suspiciously like the question, 'Is the
voter capable of knowing the best form of government
for himself?' Only the patient and his family stay with
the patient outside the practitioner's office. Only he
and his family know whether he's better or worse.
What the public is hungry for are simple facts, not
learned opinions or rationalizations. As a matter of
fact, a patient's results may be due to other factors
and influences than the practitioner himself understands."

"What do you mean?" Carl asked.

"I mean that if the energy supply or well-being is

increased for a time after Freudian treatment, it may be due to several things, among them lower ethical requirements. We know that civilized life calls for a great deal more expenditure of energy than animal life. Civilized man must furnish energy to be spent in inhibitions, in religious obligations and those of conscience, in sex restrictions, in permanent duty to parents, family and many other requirements that the animal doesn't know. We call them standards. Now the energy required by these standards may be readily saved by lowering a patient's standards nearer the less demanding ones of an animal."

"You mean regression?"

"A purposeful evolutionary regression," Michael assented. "Increased energy from regression is waiting for some mentally disturbed, but it isn't always easy to lead them to it. Higher moral standards in 'nice' patients must be systematically attacked, discredited, broken down. Conscience is exposed as an ugly evil called guilt. The wonders of God's creation and of man and his works are seen not from the brain or the heart but from the blind sack of the genital gland. Classic fiction is aborted to give monstrous meanings to long respected things like affection for parents. The latter have been especially attacked since they're the holdover of older moralities. To succeed, they must be made the villains in the piece."

Michael's voice grew unusually mild and flat as it did sometimes when very earnest and aroused. He went on.

"Naturally if you revert from the higher energy demands of civilization and of spiritual problems to something morally nearer the standards of the animal, you save a great deal of energy. In the case of saving a life or curing an otherwise hopeless psychosis, it may be justified, but hardly to save the discomfort of a neurosis."

"Even the young and healthy who never had a neurosis are propagandized in your schools and colleges," Mohammed pointed out.

"Yes, the whole movement bears a strong resemblance to the totalitarian movement. Both employ a myth-exposing, white-is-black technique. Religion, honor to parents and conscience are analyzed and discredited. Both movements call it liberating. It's also significant that the leaders of both movements hoped to convert mankind. Such a world-conquering messianic complex that ignores the unfavorable results of their own doctrines could be rationalized only by men of either great credulity or ambition or both. The intelligence of the men placed by circumstances in power in both movements may be gauged by their claims that when the world is reconstructed by their respective methods, we can expect happiness and peace."

"Both movements are very powerful," Milt pointed out.

"Going back to the primitive releases powerful primitive energies," Michael agreed gravely. "The Freudians go back not only to more primitive standards but unwittingly to the more primitive stage of our lives."

"I don't get that," Milt said.

"I mean to our youth when our energies haven't

been tapped by the million and one problems of experience added day by day as we grow older. Maturity multiplies the simple energy demands of youth. We might take a small example. When I was a boy in the country I saw grass as something fresh and green to rejoice and play in. Now as a man in the same grass I see or feel many other things. Our Western grass may be thin, won't make good hay or pasture. The horses and cows grazing in it are bony. The fences need mending. The soil is eroded. The small rancher's house is inadequate for his family. The windows are small. It has an adobe floor and no conveniences. Frijoles are the daily diet. So in my maturity the field, the ranch, the dismal background, the hard struggle for existence and many other associated cell groups of experience all take their toll of energy released by the pleasant green grass. Now if I can go back in the tree rings of my life before the expending groups of knowledge were multiplied and perhaps before the psycho-energic circuits corroded, I'll find the primitive energy stream far less dissipated, much fresher and stronger."

"You mean as it was years ago?"

"No, as it is now."

"At your age?" Carl asked.

Michael looked rueful.

"Not as strong and fresh a stream perhaps as in my youth or prime," he admitted. "But far fresher than my face and stubble and slow mind would indicate. That's why old people remember and like to talk of their youth. It brings them in touch with their energy stream at levels nearer its source, where it hasn't as yet been lost in the coils of mental experience. As a result its stronger energy content can dominate the energy-starved consciousness of age. So I suspect that if and when a psychoanalyst finds increased energy of well-being rising in a patient, it may not be due to what he thinks so much as to the deeper veins of energy struck when he digs into childhood memories. Strong energy flows are released and transferred to play on the patient's present fear deficits, some of which may be relaxed or relieved. Energy which otherwise is dissipated by the many circuits of the past can now by this short cut reach the present needs with little waste. When this cumulative surplus is strong enough to dissolve a present deficit, it may be mistakenly assumed that the memory chanced to be spoken of at the moment, especially if it carries strong energy flow, was the offending root of the trouble."

"You surprise me, Michael," Milt said.

"Energy may be applied not only from past to present but from present to past. Bringing a condition of early unhappiness or fear out into the light has no curative value except by the irrelevant analogy of microbes and sun. But speaking about it or confessing it to some listener reaches into the past where it may have little energy relief and transfer facilities available to it and connects it with the present where for the moment at least it has a great deal so that it can obtain energy from the higher levels of consciousness. These may now supply and relax it."

"Go on, Michael," Milt urged.

Michael stood up smiling, an action we had learned to know well.

"Is there any chance of taking a little ride today? Perhaps I could show you things that might give you a better idea than words."

When we left, he asked if it would be all right to drive up the mountain. At the store, he suggested taking the lefthand road. In those days it was little more than a pair of wheel tracks but it led to Cienega Canyon as now. In the canyon he took us to the spring.

"Water's a poor analogy for energy," he confessed, "but it will have to do today. This is the source of San Antonito's irrigation supply. In nature as in men we find strong sources and weak sources. This is on the weak side. Why is a weak producer? We don't always know but we know we can't do a great deal to increase its production. Blasting or surgery may not only fail to increase the flow but may divert it somewhere else. One small thing we can do is save both water and energy in times of plenty. You noticed the storage tanque at the forks. The rest of the time we must adjust consumption to supply if we wish to get along. We can't expect a weak producer to energise too much activity."

"What if you do?"

"Some fields will have poor and starved crops," Michael answered. "Bodily energy fields are similarly affected. Of course, psycho-energics is far more complex than irrigation, and you must keep that in mind. The best we can hope for is a rough engineering knowledge of life energy. Now can we go up the mountain?"

The Sandia Mountains reach up two miles above sea level. San Antonito itself is nearly seven thousand feet. A forestry road climbs through a canyon called Tejano, which means Texan. Down at Sandia Park it was like early summer when we left. Part way up the mountain we came to spring. Wild iris was in bloom. Still higher the aspens stood white and leafless. Small wild crocus-like Easter flowers still bloomed. Once we saw the dirty remnant of a snow bank deep in a north canyon. Birds were in the pines, firs and spruces. Jays flashed bright blue in the sun. The forest mould looked rich and moist. Winter was over up here and the big mountain slowly coming alive.

Still far below the top, we started down through another canyon. Presently an old road took us into ancient fields gone back to the wilderness. This was Ellis Ranch, where an Anglo family had once lived, cleared the ground, ploughed, raised crops, stock and children. Now all was abandoned. The life-giving water remained, a strong stream coming out of the granite rock and flowing lustily down the canyon. We climbed out of our cars and stood listening to its rich fertile sound in this country of little rain.

"I never come here," Michael said, "without speculating where all this water comes from. In a good snow year it runs all summer. I once took a pencil and figured how many millions of gallons it must flow in a year. I found it hard to believe that there's so much storage space in the mountain above this elevation. It's just naturally a strong producer." He was quiet a moment and added, "It's significant that not a drop of this product reaches the Rio Grande."

"Why not?" we wanted to know but he crawled

back into the car. A mile or two down the canyon he stopped us and we got out again. "Do you notice anything?" he asked with the expression of a peasant who has something interesting to show you.

"The stream isn't so loud any more," Carl said. "Either there's less fall down here or less water."

"I think there's less water," Michael nodded. "Now where did it go?"

We looked up the canyon. We knew Ellis Ranch was abandoned. There was at that time no house above us. We could see only rock, banks of yellow disintegrated granite and steep mountain slopes covered with sharp pointed firs and spruces.

"It went for nothing good anyhow," Mohammed answered.

"True enough," Michael agreed. "A little went in evaporation, but very little in this moist mountain air. Most of it was lost in rock cracks, gravel and sand traps. So a good deal of our primeval life energy is lost. Now can any of you tell me what these psycho-energic cracks, gravel pits and sand traps are?"

"Conflicts," Milt suggested.

"I think," Michael said, "we better deal with conflict for Milt before going on to real causes. The word 'conflict' is greatly overworked, Milt. This time by conflict or inner conflict I think you mean a man's desire to take two mutually contradictory courses or to be obliged to take one when the other is really desired. Now these desires don't fight with each other as the term suggests. Double, triple and multiple desires are common to most of us and are usually no cause of mental ill health. When this occurs, we must look farther to the particular desires and energy or lack of energy available."

"Will you go into this more thoroughly for me?" Milt asked.

"Let's look first at desire," Michael agreed. "Now what's the basic substance of all desire?"

"The sex impulse," Carl volunteered.

"I'm afraid that's defensive thinking or poor observation or both," Michael said. "The real organic desire is always for energy to supply expenditure. Sexual stimulation is only one of the processes releasing energy flow. Other common desires promising energy release are sport, adventure, entertainment, accomplishment, escape, fight, food, drink, money and what it buys, a career, a higher or lower level of existence, many things. Now in Milt's conflicting desires, the individual may be obliged to take a certain course for the sake of society, business, his family, appearances, reason and so forth. But for other personal and perhaps secret reasons, another course powerfully draws him. Why?"

"More energy?" Milt asked.

"More or quicker energy or both," Michael agreed. "It's true that the advised course of his reason or family may eventually lead him to much greater energy and pleasure than the other path. What his organism wants, however, is immediate, not future energy. The course it thirsts for is probably one that has strong natural, perhaps racial and primitive energy sources established in his individual nervous system. The highway of reason may be too long and austere for him. He wants to jump the fence to greener pastures and to paths more natural and energy-fruitful to him. These pastures may or may not include the possibility of mares."

"You said multiple desires are common and often no cause of mental ill health?" Milt reminded.

"That's true. In most organisms, notably those not lacking in a variety of established energy sources, nothing serious happens. It may be strong enough to follow both courses. If impossible because of their nature, the more energy-commanding desire will usually dominate and proceed with its sequence of mental release processes to find a visual solution. We call this deciding or thinking it through. The solution mentally reached relaxes expenditure. This and perhaps a painful obstruction to his lesser desire releases enough energy flow to keep the lesser group submissive. In other words, a so-called normal man has enough energy available to choose a desire, live with it and lay the other regretfully aside, at least for the time being. The desire he follows may be the one most painful if he resists it and promising richer energy relief if he takes it. It also may be the more primitive."

"Then the richer and more primitive energy desire always triumphs?"

"The richer energy desire may not be the more primitive. Higher things and their higher energy rates may command more energy in some of us than the primitive. Desire for duty and decency has often been stronger in certain men than pleasure. Holy work, even sacrifice and deprivation aren't necessarily barren, especially to the religious, but may be rich in energy. It all depends on what's been established by birth and experience in the individual."

"It's the person really hurt by inner conflict I'm interested in, Michael," Milt urged.

"Well, let's take a man in conflict who despite seeming complexity has fewer sources and transfer points of energy. As a result his welfare is more desperately affected by such few strong sources as he has to draw on. He can't substitute what he doesn't have. His sequence of mental processes tries to think a choice through but can't release enough energy along the way to reach a solution. Either course contemplated leads to mental deficit pain he can't dissolve. His distressed organism may make instinctive and convulsive breaks by pouring out energy wholesale at intervals in an attempt to reach and relax the painful deficits. Such indirected and improperly transferred energy seldom reaches the destination in quantity, is spread too thin. The effect is a kind of helpless exhaustion similar to the interrupted sequence of release processes we call frustration, as happened to Pavlov's dog. Unfulfilled desires as well as interrupted release processes abandoned in mid-sequence are left hanging unresolved and unrelieved. They go on spending energy, robbing where they can, depleting certain energy levels. They particularly upset and jangle the smooth running mechanism of other associated processes."

"Then the natural release processes of desire should always be followed like the psychiatrists say?" Carl asked.

"If they were," Michael said, "much of the real advancement and accomplishment of mankind would have been lost. The organism as a rule takes the road suitable to its psycho-energic make-up and development. If natural primitive desires are the main fountains of energy in its nervous system, it will likely follow them. If it has energy sources to supply a more austere desire, that's the one it may take or try. In either case you should understand that desire isn't the fearful and inexorable thing it's made out to be by those who want nothing to stop them from yielding to it. All that desire wants is energy. It may not always get it but when it's furnished to the certain groups desiring it, desire becomes tame as a lamb."

"If inner conflict isn't the villain in emotionally disturbed people, what is?" Carl asked.

"Now we're back to the original question before we got sidetracked with conflict," Michael said. He indicated the stream. "You remember we came to the conclusion that most of the water lost enroute disappeared in rock cracks, gravel pits and sand traps. Now in what cracks, pits and traps is our primitive stream of life energy lost?"

"Anxiety and fears," Milt suggested.

"Anxieties and fears are not causes," Michael repeated patiently. "They're release processes to provide energy to underlying deficit causes. Between anxiety and the basic cause may lie several layers of causes. For instance, anxiety is often a result of fear, which in turn may be due to the presence or recurrence of shock, which is itself an effect of something deeper. Now can anyone tell me what shock is?"

"A strong emotional disturbance paralyzing the

nervous system or producing agitation," Milt offered.

Michael shook his head slowly.

"I hear you but you don't explain anything."

"What is shock then?"

"You remember how the organism responds to danger? It summons mental and physical energy often in advance to meet the energy requirements of fight, struggle, control, or escape. Well, shock is some extreme, often sudden requirement of energy expenditure that's too high, deep, broad or prolonged to be readily supplied by the release processes and transfer points of the cell groups touched off."

"What makes it feel so terrible?"

"The extreme inner strain laid on the system when unable to supply such a large and instant sum of energy to fill the vacuum. It's the pain of this tremendous and sustained draft on the involved cell groups and release processes that we really fear. The meaning of the words 'horror' and 'terror' comes from these strain sensations and not from the object that arouses them."

"But why does it come sometimes and not others?"

"Let's go down the canyon a little farther," Michael suggested. "Perhaps I can show you."

We climbed in our cars and drove on. The road dipped steeply for several miles. In time the canyon nearly leveled off. Green fields and fruit trees began to appear, looking incredibly verdant and lush against the barren canyon slopes. As we went on, the canyon broadened and here the settlement ended. Michael had us stop near an adobe house, larger than the others. The fields around it were well fenced but the crops appeared in drought.

Michael climbed out followed by the rest of us.

"I've met Mateo Chavez, who lives here. Like the higher conscious cell groups in us, he's the product of a later and more advanced age. His methods and ideas are progressive and would probably be very fruitful if he had water. But like the more mature and advanced ideas of older people, he's on the end of the energy line. There has to be plenty and running over to reach him. During less than normal snow years, the expenditure of more primitive groups and methods nearer the source deny him his share. All his advanced ideas are helpless without it."

"You mean other people steal his water?"

"They get it first. Wherever there's water in the desert, there's a fight for it. It's the most precious thing here. Given water and reasonably level land, you'll find fields and ranches competing for the product. Water bosses can always tell you stories of those who try to get more than their share in a dry year. Some steal it from a neighboring field or ranch. Some refuse to pay for its cost in money or community work on the acequia. Some knock out the gate at night and flood their fields when it's denied them. This was especially true in the past when might was right as it still is in the code of the organism. Now what was it you asked me about before coming down here?"

"I asked why fears and anxieties come sometimes and not others," Milt repeated.

"Well, there are years when a rancher has all the water he wants for his crops. Other years when he needs it the most, water is lacking, his crops fail and he has to go into debt for pinto beans and chile to keep his family alive."

"It's the same in our country," Mohammed said.

"It's the story of our energy needs," Michael went on. "Shock comes originally when a difficult experience finds the organism without the energy to meet it. The organism may be a chronic low producer or a high producer in low energy cycle due to recent expenditure or lowered production. Otherwise, there would be no shock. Enough energy would be there to meet the situation's demands. We'd say we threw it off or got through all right. Indeed an organism of strong energy or low spending rates might not even know there was an ordeal to meet. But to an organism responding to high wide expenditure and exhausted by the violent energy demand to relieve it, shock has been established. It can recur at low times when there isn't enough energy to throw it off."

"It doesn't only come when you're low but also when you're high," Milt said.

"That's often when the reserves are very low," Michael answered quietly. "In psycho-energics we know that contrary to all notion, happiness requires energy. Active happiness consumes a great deal of energy, enthusiasm still more. When a man who thought his loved ones drowned suddenly finds them safe, he may feel only great joy. But, although he doesn't suspect it, his great joy is actually compounded of the high expenditure rates and flows of his late belief that they were dead. It's therefore depleting his energy without him knowing it."

"He knows it later on sometimes," Dennis suggested.

"Yes, when the energy flows recede, then he may become most conscious of the depletion." Michael nodded. "We call it reaction. But there's another reason why fear can come at certain times during happiness. One is more or less unguarded then. A chronically low and harried nervous system learns to post watchful tensions or relief energy flows ready to jump in the breach and relax or disarm shock or fear suggestions the moment they appear on the horizon. In happiness these sentinel flows are lulled, drawn on, diverted."

"I knew a lady once who had shock when she prayed," R. V. said.

"If a high expenditure nervous system, especially one with lurking shock fears, turns on too much intensity, it can happen without the innocent victim knowing what hit him," Michael nodded. "Intensity means a very high rate of expenditure. While the spirit rises in exaltation, the body or supplying cell groups may come close to temporary power exhaustion. In this unsuspected exhaustion, the relief flows provided by past experience to relax regular fears are impaired. Without these forces, the attacking fear or sense of depression can't be properly met, repelled and dissolved. Also during intensity the fear that gets through seems to catch and ride up on the high spending rate. It's as if the enemy found a weak spot in our lines while our troops were at prayer and then caught some of our prayer fervor to battle us."

Mohammed had been following Michael with the most peculiar expression on his face.

"But who sends these fear thoughts and anxieties?" he asked. "The evil one?"

"Nobody necessarily sends them," Michael said. "They're just one's own memories of shock and suffering consciously or unconsciously recorded. Some of them may even come down the racial or another line, although I don't pretend to know about that. Their origin is probably during infanthood, in attacks such as convulsions; or in early childhood, in severe sickness or nightmares. Some come in youth, in ordeals of love or war experiences. We might say they're the psycho-energic deficits of the ugly or unpleasant things we've either experienced, seen, heard or read about in our lifetime. It's these shock experiences and not our calm periods of enjoyment and relaxation that carry the strong energy flows. So when our organisms become desperate for energy to supply and relieve strain, they may automatically reinvoke these horror and violence groups for the sake of their high energy content."

Milt had his eyes fastened on him.

"You mean the organism punishes itself for its own energy?"

"The organism doesn't think of either punishment or reward. It simply needs energy in a hurry. It needs it in quantity and at certain transfer points. So it acts accordingly. See yourself as a great municipality of cells divided irregularly into countless overlapping groups such as wards, suburbs, religious and secular groups, political and professional organizations and so on. Now most of the houses of this municipality even in famine have food behind their locked doors. When one aroused and impoverished group frantically needs relief, it arouses and excites some closely associated group. The second alarmed group opens its doors, picks up its belongings and runs. Then the starving group can rob it like the Bedwee jump on a running caravan to despoil it."

"So that's the explanation," Milt said.

"The more desperate and frantic an emotional need for energy, the more the high-strung organism yells fire and murder to other cell groups to get relief for itself. If self-despoiling has been going on for some time, relief flows may thin and last only a very short while. Afterward the organism is worse off than before, because still more robbed and depleted cells have been added to the deficit sum and must be satisfied. The body seldom reasons or learns. It keeps on conjuring up all its terrible thoughts to milk high energy content of shock and violence groups. The deficit and tension may finally grow so painful that the organism can't raise any more energy by fear thoughts but must go into action, beating, throwing things, shooting, destroying. It's all done to obtain energy from the stronger energy flows of violence and its consequences. Of course, the strongest flows are those provided by murder and suicide and their consequences."

"What are these efforts to get energy called?" Carl asked.

Michael looked at him in surprise.

"You mean in psycho-energics or commonly? You've been hearing them named right along. They're

R processes, release processes, more strictly relief proc-esses. In medicine and psychology they're called by different names—furors, compulsive neuroses, hysteria, compensation and so on. Compensation, for instance, is believed to be a desire to be sick in order to obtain attention. However, the real and original reason one may have a desire to be sick is to obtain energy not from another's attention, which is a windfall that afterward may become the object sought, but from himself. Such a one will groan to himself far from another's ears. The same is true when someone ap-parently wants to keep on being sick. The body wants to hold the status quo of the illness energy flows it may have been drinking from."

"That wouldn't be the reason why someone holds to his fears?" Milt asked.

Michael nodded. "Sometimes trying to take a fear away from its victim seems to generate much more fear. The body will fight to retain this energy-release source, and if you take it away, may set up still more fearful energy sources to replace it. The wise thing is to provide healthy replacement energy for certain groups of an organism before depriving them of their unhealthy energy sources."

"The first day we met you, Michael," Dennis said, "you told us we weren't ready yet to understand the real reason why trouble or hardship leaves its mark on one child and not another. I think I see it now."

Michael looked at him keenly.

"I'm sure you do. The child with too high expendi-ture potential or too little energy or both at the time of trouble is the one roped and branded by it. His identical twin, if he has one, would probably be, too. But his non-identical twin or non-twin brother and sister with lower rates or higher resources or both may not even be aware there was any trouble to endure. Even if he is aware, the lower response of his more sluggish nervous system may not set off enough expenditure to deplete him. Also, his strong energy resources may supply energy to meet the shock and let him ride over it. Most children who aren't hurt have a combination of these factors."

"Then it's pretty tough to be sensitive?" Dennis said.

"Perhaps. But there are counter balances. For instance, he has the painful advantage usually of his upper or conscious groups being robbed rather than his lower ones."

"What does that mean?" Milt asked skeptically.

"Well, we've seen that the organism must rob energy somewhere. It's the psycho-energic business of life. If it robs from vital centers, your upper conscious self may remain happy and energetic, but disease can follow in the vital cell group field of such robbings. On the other hand, if your conscious or dominating cell groups have high rates, which means that they have strong energy flows, your organism is likely to rob from these instead of from your automatic nervous system. There's a lot more conscious discomfort in this but not so much danger. Doctors frequently find nothing organically wrong with sensitives and hypochondriacs. On the other hand, by stimulants, training or resolve a sensitive may high-pressure enough energy from his system to lead a busier and richer life.

His sense of health and well-being will certainly be increased. But his liability to organic ill health seems to be also. 'Isn't it a pity?' his friends may say, 'that after being cured of all that nervousness, then he gets heart trouble?' "

"Well, I'm glad there's something good in being nervous," Milt said.

"Oh, there are other counter balances," Michael told him. "It's true that the sensitive is a perfect sitting duck for shock because of his great expenditure capabilities. On the other hand, he's often made aware at an early age of being different from the average and learns painfully to do something about it. He may get to know his limitations and how to throw energy into the breach. He also hasn't too many illusions about himself. He knows he must from the beginning learn how to supply his energy deficiencies. So he's less dependent on outside encouragement. In fact he may resent encouragement not based on fact."

"If the sensitive isn't hurt most by shock, who is?"

"The insensitive is less liable to it, and when shock hits him, he's less equipped to handle it."

"What do you mean by an insensitive?"

Michael considered.

"Let's go back up the canyon again. But first will you take us down further before you turn around?"

As soon as we left the Chavez place, we were in the desert or semi-desert. Here was dust and sand that had never known the blade of the plough. Rattlesnake weed grew along with other plants of arid and over-grazed areas, with occasional tufts of brownish grass, scattered cane, prickly pear and pincushion cactus, and a few low twisted cedars. Before turning around on the top of the second hill, there was spread out before us a vast and barren terrain.

"I think we can get an idea here what life is like deprived of normal amounts of precious life-giving product," Michael said. "Look how tiny an oasis of life really is in the desert. You can hardly make out the thin green line of the Rio Grande. Notice the neuroses of the cedars down here where water is scarce."

As we came back to the cultivated end of the canyon, Michael had us stop and get out. He pointed.

"That small adobe house up there belongs to a Baca. I think his name is Arsenio. He's one of the first on the acequia madre, has early call on water. His crop never dries up. Not that he has much, either plenty or want. Like most natives here he seldom puts anything aside. He lives for the day, like his father and grandfather did, with a couple acres of ground, a few apricot trees and a corral. You can't change him because he's never had to learn anything new or listen to anybody. He's mostly Indian. If water would suddenly peter out, he wouldn't know what to do. He's always had it, leaned on it, never worked for anybody, probably never hauled leña to town. He might endure like a stone, but it would go pretty hard with his family. His wife would likely have to go to work for some of the ricos or Anglos in Bernalillo."

He squinted.

"Now what did I say I'd tell you up here? What were we talking about?"

"I asked you what you meant by an insensitive?" R. V. said.

Michael remembered.

"By an insensitive I mean someone with enough energy available to quiet his expenditure; more specifically, a child or man with an instrument of only relatively moderate spending rates and strong primitive ego control of them. These often go together, the ego deterring painful mental spending. Now by primitive ego I don't mean it's stupid or barbarian. The primitive ego may be found in successful business and professional people, in the artistic and sophisticated, also in psychiatrists who without it wouldn't readily be drawn to what would otherwise be an extremely painful field of work or be able to keep their sanity in it. The term 'ego' doesn't intend any abstruse or abstract meaning but is an actual something: the sum of a man's dominant cell groups and energy flows, those that control him. The mark of the strong primitive ego type is that it acts constantly to protect itself, its nervous system and fleshy organism from the pain of energy loss and deficit. It does this by letting few suggestions unfavorable to its own selfhood through, including the unfavorable suggestion that it won't let such unfavorable suggestions through."

"You mean there's a censor?"

"The natural law of dominance of cell groups according to their energy expenditure, together with the effort of the organism to subordinate a painful cell group to the subconscious where it has less drain on and control of the nervous system, are often mistaken for censorship. To forget means that the forgotten cell group activity is succeeded in dominance or consciousness for the time being by cell groups of stronger energy expenditure. Some of this stronger volume reaches the painful group and so helps it in the process of subordination, partly supplying and quieting it to the subconscious from which, however, it may break out according to the volume of expenditure remaining active in it."

Michael glanced at us sharply to see if we followed him. He went on.

"Now let's look how one form of trouble, a mistake or shortcoming, is handled by the sensitive and the insensitive. The sensitive is most likely to see his mistake or shortcoming, and if he doesn't see it at the time, it may occur to him spontaneously later on, perhaps in the night. Whenever it comes, it is painful and leaves its mark so that he's likely to remember and catch himself next time. The insensitive, on the other hand, seldom easily sees his mistake or shortcoming, and if he wakes up in the night to brood, it's not over his mistake or shortcoming but some associate's unjust accusation of such a failing on his part."

"Go on, Michael," Carl requested.

"A sensitive usually can say, 'I'm sorry. I was wrong.' He knows he's often wrong and sorry and it means no more painful expenditure than he's accustomed to in his own thought. The insensitive, on the other hand, has no such experience or energy available to his thought. A simple admission like that is almost impossible for him to make. He must go to great length to destroy completely the existence or possibility of his mistake or failing, and if he can't do that, at least his painful responsibility in connection with the thing. He does this in many ways, denying or belittling it, laughing it off, ignoring it often by walking away and busying himself with something else, whitewashing his responsibility, setting up elaborate, often learned, defense, or dissipating the mistake by bringing up some other subject, by substituting admission of a much less painful error or by declaring the mistake common to everyone, to be expected and unimportant. He's adept at rebuttal, at protective replies and return questions, still more adept in making his fault a virtue, done with forethought, for some specific and worthy cause. This is only a handful of his repertory. He's done it so often, he's an expert. His technique of turning aside inharmonious suggestions before they spend his energy saves a great deal, surrounds his selfhood with energy resources with which to protect itself and beat off any bit of truth that might be painful."

"I should think that would be healthy and good. We're told that self-esteem is about the best and healthiest thing we can have."

"So long as a strong primitive ego remains undisturbed, it's harmonious to itself, although not always to everyone who comes in contact with it. However, the cards have been stacked against strong self-esteem. Life has a habit of interrupting, of breaking the status quo. A strong ego believes so much in his own capabilities that he often expects work and relationship above himself. He enters conditions he isn't naturally equipped for and which have problems he can't easily solve. At this level he's more liable to make mistakes or show shortcomings which his selfhood can't admit. If a blunder or failing of proportion overwhelms him, especially in front of others, he's left nearly naked, because his self-esteem has been the source of energy for his life and he's had little else. Such a person may willfully sicken and die sooner than admit a serious failing or mistake. To admit it would cut off the steady flow of pain-repellent energy from the ego and seems to him the destruction of his whole world. Or his ego may turn for energy to nonfactual sources whose fancied integrity he protects as he did his superiority or self-sufficiency."

"What can you do for him?"

"All of us need some ego. Those with strong self-esteem need less as the sensitive needs more. Less ego lets more painful truth and hence reality through. But you've got to be careful trying to alter the strong ego, especially the adult, or you'll tear down the whole structure built up over generations to keep a particular racial line, deficient as it is in certain things, equal to the demands of the world about it. A human being is a delicately adjusted series of cell group responses and energy-release processes. In some primitive egos— that is, with strong self-esteem—you may find a wonderful personality. You may think he or she would be still better with less ego and more sensitivity. However, in nearly all cases these attractive qualities derive their energy substance from their ego. Deflate that, and the qualities shrivel. Their source of life has been shut off."

"Why are strong egos difficult to help?"

"Because they haven't had a thousand and one frank facings of truth about themselves in the past to establish energy-release processes and transfer points to admit and relieve trouble. Their one great energy source was enough for their needs. As a result if energy deficits actually overtake them, their nervous systems' facilities to dissolve such deficits are limited."

"Then the ego type is less desirable than the sensitive?"

"It all depends whether you look at it presently or evolutionarily. Our planet couldn't do without strong egos. They carry on the business of the world. They're often cheerful or at least calm in situations that would torture and kill sensitives. Many make excellent and buoyant companions. They get more out of life, know on the whole less torment and pain. You've noticed perhaps that when you have well-being, it's easier to carry on, to be insensitive, to overlook. There's more energy available to overflow into the system and so relax deficit groups as they are touched off. Strong egos may lack higher mental and spiritual sources, but they seldom suffer from that."

"What release processes can the sensitive use to relieve anxiety, fear, and other deficits?" Milt asked.

"Man has found a good many, Milt. Some are old, some new. Some are good, some less good. But the best of them are mental. This is such a large and important field that I think we better wait to talk about it some other day."

"Well, how about a few physical R processes that help?"

"You know most of them—setting off energy flows by walking, working with the hands, playing, participation in sport which is physical activity triggered by a mental factor called game. A change of scene, people and work is extremely good. The cell groups constantly touched off by one environment, scene, work and people grow depleted in a sensitive. A change touches off new group-combinations, taps their fresh unexpended energy, giving the cell groups representing the old scene, people and work time to rest and acquire energy until returned to again. A change of altitude is also good, perhaps a daily change, sleeping at one elevation and working at another. The higher elevation increases the metabolism and spending of energy. A lower elevation lessens it, relaxes."

"What's the best place for a nervous sensitive to live?"

"I'd say where there's relaxing warmth, sun, perspiration, fresh air, everything that's conducive to a healthier body tone, which means vitality, more energy production. Living and sleeping in the open air increase energy production, tend to relieve lesser fears and anxieties, gradually resolve them. Training one's self to sleep with fresh cool air blowing on the face is the greatest single physical benefit I know. It will often put a worried and nervous sensitive to sleep and restore his energy till morning. Breathing more and deeper when awake also increases energy production, but it should be accompanied by increased physical and mental poise and morale to consume the oxygen."

Milt braced up, took a deeper breath or two, and nodded.

"Thanks, Michael," he said. "I think I actually felt it that time."

Michael looked around to get his bearings.

"Now I'd like to take you up the road a bit. Do you

mind walking? The physical R process should do us good."

He led us a short way toward the mountain. Presently he turned off and we began climbing the canyon slope. Here well above the road so it could reach the higher fields by gravity was the acequia madre running fresh and cool and nearly full. Grass, weeds and desert flowers flourished on its bank.

"You remember the primitive stream of precious stuff that I told you still flowed in most of us?" Michael asked. "Here it is before it's been fought over, robbed, appropriated and dissipated by use. If you look closely, you'll see that man on its banks is more primitive too. His fields are smaller and narrower. The biggest and best house in sight is a two-room jacal. I don't think it has an outhouse. Over there behind those bushes two children are spying on us. If you look sharp, you'll see they have a large admixture of Indian blood."

"The water looks good," Carl said.

"Yes, the strong primitive energy stream inside of us is very pleasant and life-giving. You can try to go back and live on its banks if you like. But you should know what you're doing. Of course, if you lived up here on the acequia madre, you'd have water. You'd also have certain inescapable primitive conditions and relationships to contend with. So if you go back to live on the bank of your primitive energy stream, there may be conditions which parts of you might object to and cause you more energy expenditure and unhappiness in the end than what you save in primitive pleasure."

He bent down and straightened up with a stem of grass in his fingers.

"The alternative is to try to hold your relative stage of development, whatever it happens to be. I mean your peculiar individual sensitiveness and standards. This means, of course, retaining much of your high energy-spending capabilities, including the pain rates that build energy flows, which is the system that brought man up to where he is. You may have a prism in you of such quality that you prefer to see the light of life through it rather than through a grosser and cloudier glass that filters out the sometimes painful brightness."

He looked thoughtfully down the canyon at the arid region.

"If you do decide to stand your ground and hold your own, you should understand that there's nothing sinister or significant in the feeling of your low-energy pressure periods and sensations. Ordinarily such sensations frighten, adding greatly to the expenditure and energy load, often sending the patient into fear tensions that spend a great deal more than the original deficit. Then too, many of the sensations of non-well-being that a moderately well man has from day to day but never notices are interpreted as symptoms of being mentally or emotionally unwell."

Michael chewed his grass and went on.

"A man should remember that he would have much of these anyway. As for the genuine symptoms of nervous exhaustion, they are just the strain of a mechanism short of energy, and any seeming chemical changes such as coppery taste are the fumes of lean mixture and poor combustion. Without its full and usual power, the engine can't work as smoothly as you've been accustomed to, and this puts a strain on the rest of the mechanism. It's like a man who worked for you before and always performed his tasks quietly. Day or night you hardly knew he was there. But now you haven't enough money to pay him. He works under protest and the rest of the time hangs around and pickets you, straining your relations with other employees and leaving a bad taste in your mouth. But that's about as far as he goes if you handle him wisely, and once you pay him back, he'll be his old faithful self again."

When we went down the bank, Michael helped R. V., then laid his arm over Milt's shoulder.

"How about riding back with us, Milt?" he asked.

Milt and he sat together on the back seat. Although I listened sharply as I drove, nothing much was said. Michael seemed unusually deep in thought, and Milt his old self, talking of things we saw on the way, a mule deer in the firs and the view from our favorite place where the road hugged the side of the mountain. Michael scarcely spoke till we drew up at the familiar blue door. Since then I've wondered about it, remembering the dish of lamb and the wild tale the Mexican boys told about Michael and the wounded bird.

CHAPTER NINE

SOME MENTAL AND SPIRITUAL
ENERGY SOURCES

"I have meat to eat that ye know not of."

JESUS CHRIST

NEXT SUNDAY Michael wasn't at home. Nor was Celso at his house. It was San Juan's Day, and San Juan was the patron saint of San Antonio, so we drove down. The village was decked with wild flowers and pine boughs. Booths with ramadas for roofs had been set up. The boys said they had noticed the decorations when they drove through but hadn't seen Michael. We all saw him now in the line of natives setting out to bless the spring.

He beckoned us to join him, which we did. Priests from Albuquerque led the procession followed by guitar players. Behind them came a long line of women in bright colors. Men and boys brought up the rear. Michael walked with the village juez de paz. We were in pairs behind him. Our way led up through the meadows. It reminded me of Delacroix's painting of the gay marriage procession through the grassy French countryside. I think we were the only Anglos. The Mexicans are musical and all joined in the singing, which was in Spanish, serious hymns going up to the spring, and lively, joyous ones coming back.

There would be festivities all day, Michael said, and his native friends counted on him to stay. He wouldn't be free until after mass in the early evening. Did we care to come back for church?

We returned in the late afternoon. The old adobe church was crowded with natives, many standing in the rear. At special times during the mass a musket was shot off outside. Services over, we came out to find the road on both sides lighted by burning pine wood. The ancient village scene, the piles of blazing faggots, the red fire flickering on dark, unfamiliar faces was like something from the Middle Ages. Even R. V. was moved by it. He told us he could feel and almost see it. Afterward we got in our cars. Michael with us, and drove to his house in San Antonito.

It was now growing dark but the luminous pale-green belt, which comes after June sunsets at these altitudes, still glowed around the horizon like a great band of Saturn.

"I don't feel like sitting in the house tonight," Michael said. "How about going up the ladder?"

We lifted his pine bench to the flat roof. Some of us sat on the adobe curb of the house. It was very pleasant up there, the village dim and peaceful around us after the lights and excitement of San Antonio. We watched the green belt of the planet fade and the stars grow bright and living overhead.

"You said last week you'd tell us about the richest of all energy sources," Milt reminded him.

Michael stayed silent a long time. He seemed reluctant to leave the substantial world of matter for the imponderable one of thought.

"Yes, our mental and spiritual sources," he acknowledged finally. "We happen to be practising one of them right now."

"You mean the peace and quiet?" Carl asked.

"Peace and quiet after the activity of the fiesta," Michael pointed out. "First the activity, then the peace and quiet. Don't underestimate the first part. It arouses the energy flows so they may be released and enjoyed when the expenditure stops. It's the more important of the two factors. The second would be ineffective without it."

"What do you call this practise?" Dennis asked.

"The second part I call contracting the energy expenditure. The alternating expanding and contracting of our expenditures is the most important life process I know. We'll look at the whole process some other time. Today we want to look chiefly at contraction."

"Can you give us another example?"

"I could give you a good many. One form is narrowing the radius of expenditure. This contracts energy consumption. If ever you're bored or jaded with the world, shut yourself up in a dim room and look out of a small hole or crack. You'll see a world more interesting than the one you just left."

"How's that possible?" Carl asked skeptically.

"Try it sometime. When you're bored or discouraged, your lowered energy flows may be too thin or scattered to power clearly the wide scenes, activities and implications of the outside world. A much narrowed radius of both sight and association needs far less energy to power it. The energy is concentrated in a tiny radius of expenditure, so there's plenty now to illuminate what little of the world you see and feel."

"I can understand that," R. V. said.

"Civilized man feels superior to the savage," Michael went on. "But when some of our civilized explorers live the savage life, they tell us that the savage knows life more fully and feels it more richly than we do. One reason is that his energy is less diffused over the wide range of civilization's knowledge and experience. Instead, it's concentrated on simple things; on just living, seeing and feeling. His energy isn't dissipated, wasted by so many pawns. In psycho-energics we know that what counts is never pawns, what we call things, but the energy connected with them in our nervous system."

"What do we laymen call this process of narrowing the radius of expenditures?" Dennis asked.

"We call it escape—retreat—giving up the world—going native—entering a convent or monastery—cutting down our activities—giving up our ambitions—going out in the desert to pray—locking ourselves in our room—retiring to a cabin to write a book—even going to jail, where some excellent books have been written. All these practises are most useful when temporary. If permanent, the limited scope is apt to become normal, and the energy flows from life problems and experiences dry up. But if temporary, unused cell groups save energy for useful expenditure later on. It's like leaving off milking till morning when the cow's ready to be milked again. That's all right. But if you leave off milking entirely harm can come to the cow and its milk processes."

He stopped and peered at us. He looked tired even in the dimness.

"Let's see now, how many mental energy sources have I given you?"

"You gave us only one tonight—contracting the radius of expenditure," we said.

"Well, we can also cut down the rate of expenditure—slow up. When we're in the pink, we find we may do things rapidly with little effort. The magic energy currents are there. The interlocking release processes of a sequence run into each other smoothly and without strain. But when energy is low, we don't have the power. Now if a locomotive is short on steam, it naturally and mechanically slows up. But the life organism and especially the human organism has far more energy resources than the locomotive and has evolved facilities to draw on them and step up the lowered energy. As you know, we call these facilities release processes. In the case of a sensitive low in energy, there are certain release processes he is more likely to use to keep him going. He may complain, criticize, curse, but this, as we've learned, brings him small actual energy. An R process that provides him more of a step-up in energy is tension."

"What about tension?" Milt urged.

"Well, as I think was mentioned once before, tensions are secondary cell groups set off to be robbed for their energy content. Before throwing the shot or making a high jump, you tense a physical part of you. It helps provide for your muscular effort, gives you greater power. You do the same before or while the dentist drills. The organism is trying to release energy to transfer to those cell groups made energy-deficient by the expenditure of present or expected effort or pain. You clench your hands, curl your toes, set your jaw muscle and may do one or more of a thousand other things you don't notice."

"Isn't that good?"

"It's all right for throwing the shot or making a high jump perhaps, anything once and done. Then the tension group soon recovers its energy. But if tension of the same group is done too often or continuously, the robbery channel is maintained. The tensed part can't relax. It involves other groups in its efforts to get energy relief and may tie up the body in a tension field. Long before this, the release process has become a liability."

"What physical part of us do we tense most?"

"Individual organisms tend to fall into individual tension habits. One of the most common and disastrous tensions is of the eye."

"The eye?" Milt murmured.

"It tenses against bright light and to see better in dim light. It tenses to release extra energy against the deficits of painful or unpleasant sights, including people or objects we dislike. When the organism remembers unpleasant or unhappy incidents, it often sees them in the mind's eye, and then the physical eye tension may be repeated unbeknownst to us. To provide release processes to this particular tension, the organism may blink, screw up the face, pull or finger the nose or mustache and practise other small relief processes which deliver the energy as physically close to the need as possible. Of course, the organism may also involve more serious mental and physical groups far from the eye but which have some association or transfer point to it."

"What, for instance?"

"Well, two common tensions the organism uses for energy, particularly the sensitive or high-strung organism, are hurry and undue intensity."

"I've noticed that when I'm tensed I hurry," Milt said. "Why do I do it?"

"You hurry because the excitement of hurry releases energy to the energy deficit in you that sets it off. You also often hurry to obtain energy more quickly. In the low energy conditions of tension there may not be enough energy available to power each physical movement smoothly, so you rush both mentally and physically to the next step or act of the movement to release energy to relieve the strain of the last. Starved nervous systems also arouse energy by turning on more power, intensity or emotion than the situation requires. It's like money being scarce. You know you won't get ten dollars if you ask for it, so you make a great fuss demanding a hundred and get ten. Hurry and intensity are like that, a considerable fuss to insure a bit of energy."

"What can a fellow do about tension and hurry?" Milt asked.

"Why don't you just relax, Milt?" Dennis suggested.

"I can't," Milt told him.

"Only the strong have energy to relax," Michael commented.

"You mean it takes energy to relax?" Carl asked incredulously.

"For years well-meaning doctors and friends have been telling us, just relax, take it easy, expecting us to do it. But to the sensitive, it's extremely difficult. The strong can use energy from overflow or surplus. The weak must set off release processes to provide the energy flow. Because of the closer relation between active groups, it's easier to transfer energy to the act of keeping going than to relax."

"There must be some way."

"Let's look at relaxation first. When you can do it, relaxation is one of the most efficient of release processes. It resolves cell group expenditures, saving and releasing the energy as long as the flow continues, then storing it. However, the act of physical relaxation or energy saving needs to be first primed by energy. The man with energy available can lean back at any time at his desk, put his feet on it and thus save both the energy of the priming and relaxation. The man with energy deficit is often able to let go only in the morning in bed when it's time to get up, after rest has saved and accumulated enough energy during the night to perform the act of relaxation."

"Where does that leave me?" Milt complained.

"If priming energy isn't available to the necessary groups, you must provide it. Both priming and relaxation may be done unconsciously. When we're discouraged, we may lower our heads in our hands or throw ourselves on the bed. We call it giving way to discouragement. The real motive of the act, however, is a form of relaxation—to save energy by a more nearly horizontal position and also by shutting out energy-consuming objects from sight. Discouragement provides the priming energy necessary for the act. Getting down on our knees to pray or lying flat on the ground before God or some ruler as practised in the East had its origins in the same psycho-energic urge. It's a kind of relaxation to save energy toward the emotional deficit that caused the man to pray or fear in the first place. In this case the emotional need or fear provides the priming energy. Today man calls these acts symbols of humility or defenselessness, not understanding their psycho-energic purpose."

"What if unconscious priming isn't enough?"

"Then he must practise conscious priming. For instance, if you were a tensed and hurrying rookie in the army, a tough sergeant might bawl at you to slow down. His order undoubtedly would release enough priming energy in you to let you obey. So also if you were a child and your father, who you knew meant business, ordered you to do it. Also, your doctor or a nurse might take hold of your arm and say, 'Let go—just let go,' and enough energy might be set off by the contact to perform it. However, in all these cases the control of your energy comes from outside yourself and you can't depend on that. One purpose of growth is to set up your own controls and energy-release processes."

"How do I do that?" Milt asked.

"One way to release energy for relaxation is to ex-

ecute your own mental order to let go and do it as if
you meant business. Often you can release some priming energy to relax by words—by repeating over and
over that your body and eyes are relaxed. A physical
form of priming is the R process of setting the jaw
and so releasing energy to relax and slow up other
parts of the body. Another mental process is to fore-
see the painful results of hurrying and tension on
your heart, health, dignity and the opinion of others.
A powerfully unpleasant picture will release enough
energy to relax some of the tension. This is a particularly efficient method because it transfers energy directly from the painful mental picture to the hurrying
or tension groups which are themselves contained in
the same group combination."

We sat quiet for a while during which I thought I
felt Milt relax. But only for a while. He started to stir.

"That's two general mental sources of energy," he
said.

Michael sighed.

"Well, for our third, let's take a very different
source of energy, an effective release process we seldom use when we need it but only when we don't.
For instance when we have the energy surplus of happiness or contentment, we often run our mind over
the good things we have and the pleasant enjoyments
ahead, tapping the energy of each to increase our sum
of pleasure. Now unfortunately in unhappiness or dis-
content, our nervous system turns instinctively for
energy relief not to these small surpluses but to the
groups known as troubles, problems, worries, resentment, self-pity and such. It does this because these

groups are never entirely at rest and can be aroused and contacted more easily. Also they carry richer energy booty, which tempts robbery. But these groups have so much more demand over supply that they resist strenuously. The energy yielded is small and brief. Activating these groups adds more deficit to the organism. It's like needing money and going around to all your debt-ridden friends to borrow from because they're easier to approach. They lend you a trifle, which is all they can spare, but now you've given them a basis to borrow from you in return, so that in time you are deeper in debt than ever. A wise man goes around collecting from solvent friends who can lend or give him out of their surplus without hurting themselves. The shrewd organism does the same, borrowing from its benign and solvent cell groups which can spare energy without hurting themselves or the cell community."

I don't think any of us were sure what he was talking about.

"What are these benign and solvent cell groups?" R. V. asked.

"Groups which have energy resources to relax themselves. In other words, good and beneficial facts —things we've accomplished—things satisfactory and harmonious—things belonging to us and already paid for in either sweat or money—the comforts of a roof, shelter in winter, a bed to lie on, blankets to keep us warm—the boon of sun, air, stars, earth, beauty, of parents, brothers, friends, neighbors, companionship, not being alone in the world—sanctions and sufferance given us—the illnesses, cripplings, misfortunes we've escaped—privileges we have like our being alive and having energy to move and faculties to see, hear, feel and think. Imagine how the man in the grave would leap for our chance at life. The number of our energy assets is legion. The wise man will make a mental list of his own and go over it regularly as a devotion. Especially when he's low in energy or spirit. The energy each solvent cell group yields will be as honey. If he strings enough of such groups together, his released surplus energy will reach a tidy sum. Even though he's in prison, the cell will glow with a golden light. That golden light is the glow of energy."

We were moved by his words.

"What do you call this process, Michael?" Mohammed asked.

"Just one of the Conscious or Controlled Relief processes. I call them C R processes for short. Unfortunately you call this particular process by such sweet and pious terms as looking on the bright side, counting your blessings, gratitude and thanksgiving. Actually it's not a religious act but a hardheaded and realistic process. It's not a state of mind, must be actually done like any other mental work. Only then it yields its energy for well-being. The man who doesn't use it but thinks of his troubles instead is like a general who fights only with his weak and worn-out front-line troops and never calls on his strong, well-fed army waiting in reserve."

"Shouldn't gratitude be to God?" Mohammed asked.

"All gratitude for good is instinctively to the Creation and its Creator. If you make it a holy requirement, the act is likely to become deficient in energy, and there's no energy surplus to harvest."

Michael sighed and leaned back, looking out over the dark plain where a distant solitary yellow light twinkled among the cedars.

"That's three mental energy sources," Milt prompted. "Are there any more?"

I felt R. V.'s sightless eyes on the weaver as if he could actually see him.

"Michael's tired, Milt," he said. "He's had a busy day. We ought to sit here and let him rest."

Michael looked toward him quickly. I couldn't see his face but his voice had warm affection.

"R. V.'s practising another C R process right now; one of the most powerful sources of energy and in one of the richest energy fields. Now what are our richest energy fields?"

"Trouble, fear, shock," Dennis suggested.

"That's a strong one but there's another."

"Getting mad, hating somebody?" Carl guessed.

"That's good enough. We know that anger, hate, dislike, injustice, resentment, vengeance, bitterness, feud and war establish rich and powerful energy flows in connection. Though these flows are high, the expenditure or consumption in most of us is much higher still, which means deficit or pain. But man's evolved a process to resolve this powerful expenditure and so release the rich energy connected with it. Can any of you tell me what it is?"

We had pricked up our ears not only at what he intimated but at something new in his voice. He no longer seemed tired as he went on.

"We dislike someone, perhaps hate him for what he's done to us. It takes a great effort for most of us to summon energy to overcome that hate and resentment. But once we accomplish it, we overpower and relax the expenditure which may be robbing large sums of energy from us and take command of the now liberated energy flows. Can anybody tell me what this act is called?"

"Love?" R. V. suggested.

Michael assented.

"It's an energy stream born of many sources, whatever can contribute to a strong enough volume to overcome and relax the hate expenditure. Once our technique grows, we add to the stream by releasing the energy of other and deeper hate groups within us. We might call the love process a psycho-energic pipe inserted deeper and deeper beneath the crater of the human volcano, tapping more and more of the ugly power, not only eliminating the threat of eruption but running off the violent explosive heat to warm and power our own and our neighbors' houses. Love saves far more energy than it expends. It's therefore the most efficient of release processes, being self-supporting and having energy surplus left for other organisms. Like gratitude, it's a mistake to think of it as pious, sentimental or religious. It's one of the greatest sources of practical energy in the world and may be found in a pagan as well as a Christian."

"Your sources of love shock me a little, Michael," Dennis declared.

"The Creator's methods often shock the orthodox," Michael said. "Some think of love as a kind of unchangeable element handed down pure from the Creator. They're disturbed by the suggestion that it may be born of so-called evil. They would be repelled by the thought that it taps the pits of personal and perhaps ancestral hates deep inside of them, and especially that the greater the hate or violence in a man or his past, the greater the love potential established. This potential may never be converted into love during the man's lifetime. But when it is finally so converted, you have a more powerful love than in the man who's been mild and good all his life."

"Isn't that terribly unjust?" Dennis wanted to know.

"It's simple psycho-energic law, sometimes slow, sometimes fast, but always cumulative and efficient. The forces of hate literally and evolutionarily become the forces of love. Stock raisers know that the wild colt invariably makes a better horse than the tame one. We're told there's more rejoicing in heaven over the sinner who repents than over the ninety and nine who have no need of repentance. Repenting is disavowing and resolving bad expenditure, releasing the sinner's powerful energy for good. So the repentant sinner is a stronger asset to the Creator on the average than the man mild and pious from birth. If not sinners, at least violent natures were invariably chosen for great roles in the Bible. Moses had killed an Egyptian. David had killed his tens of thousands. Peter, who was to cut off the ear of the high priest's servant with his sword, was selected to found the Christian church. Paul had persecuted, jailed and perhaps stoned to death early Christians. Even Christ cursed the fig tree, bitterly denounced the Pharisees and drove the money changers out of the temple."

"Your hate-to-love process explains a verse in the Old Testament," Milt said. " 'The wrath of man shall praise thee.' It's in the Psalms. I never understood it before."

"We mustn't be repelled by the seemingly evil sources of some of the Creator's good," Michael declared. "Our job is to try to understand it."

We spoke a long time about good and evil. It was getting late, already past Michael's bedtime. I think he was well aware of it because he went to the next point on his own.

"One mental source of energy for imaginative people is to establish a make-believe R process to release energy to needy dominant groups and relieve them."

I thought I saw Carl sit up.

"You mean a make-believe R process will actually release energy?"

"Oh, yes. As a matter of fact, most of our fears and even many of the so-called real things that set off our R processes in life are only pawns, make-believe, don't actually exist."

"How do you set up an imaginative R process?" Milt asked.

"Well, if you're bored with life and place, you may imagine yourself in a much worse, unhappy place, say at war, on a foreign shore, in prison, in a steamy mosquito-ridden jungle where you might easily be and where men of your own country generally are at the moment. If your imagination is good, high expenditure will be set off. Comparison with your present place will release and transfer the energy flows of the greater expenditure to relieve the lesser, bathing your present place, making it seem better and more desirable."

Michael's voice sounded lazy as he went on.

"The imaginative energy-release process can be adjusted to many problems. Suppose you can't sleep for noise from street traffic. You can imagine yourself lost, buried and abandoned in the black, endless silence of a cave. Or you can make believe that war has destroyed our cities, gas refineries and wells and so silenced our millions of cars. Now the sound of traffic means you're out of the cave, that the war's over. This resolves the high expenditure of war and its destruction, releasing the energy which, when transferred to the noise of traffic, resolves its deficits or at least lowers them, making it bearable. Before you know it, you're likely to find yourself asleep as I nearly am now."

"What if a factory or steel mill keeps you awake?" Carl asked.

"Well, you might imagine yourself owner of or worker in the mill which has been out of operation so long that you've become poor, perhaps hungry. Now its noise means resumption of work, food, security. This resolves the expenditure of being out of work, releasing its energy to be applied to its noise at night, making it sound pleasant."

He yawned and went on.

"Don't smile. There was a time when such imagined correctives were as real and effective as drugs. If they're less so today, it's a sign of the loss of controlled imagination in both children and men due to the lack of necessity of providing their own amusement and to their living in a very material world."

"Can I go down and make you some coffee, Michael?" Carl asked.

"No, thanks, Carl, I think it's our talk that's releasing energy, relaxing me and making me sleepy. We never talked of these things at night before. All these potential energy sources, I suspect, have been planted in life. Man just finds and adapts them to his purpose. Those processes that work and yield him energy, he keeps using. There are three we haven't touched on as yet. They're three of the most effective. One of them man's been using for thousands of years. I mean prayer."

"Has psycho-energics learned anything new about prayer?" Mohammed asked.

"Most of us know," Michael reflected, "the classic source of energy from prayer, namely God. What we don't realize is that the petitioner's fervency and desperation in the act of prayer may arouse strong energy flows in himself. Some of these flows reach the painful deficit groups which form the needy situation for which the petitioner prays. There is a reduction of deficit in the pain, sickness, misfortune or whatever lack is prayed about. The petitioner feels more hopeful, stronger. He rises refreshed, sometimes with the feeling he's been in contact with divine sources, and he has."

"How can he have been in contact with divine sources when the energy came from himself?" Milt asked.

"The savage sees his gods in stones, mountains and

lightning," Michael reminded. "We must look a little deeper. First we should understand that all is God's creation. The Creator doesn't necessarily have to attend us in person any more than He personally and individually lifts sap from the tree's roots to its leaves. He has provided processes. We might say that when the petitioner gets energy from himself he taps the God power or process in himself. Some of this power comes from his God-concept, the combination of energy flows he's built up by many things in the groups of his mental, physical and spiritual experience with God."

"You mean there is no personal God who answers prayer?" Mohammed inquired.

"No, I don't mean that. Principles and processes established by a great creative mind to stand for itself don't eliminate the existence of the mind and its being. For example, a great engineer and benefactor may provide wells in the desert to quench the thirst of those who live there or pass by. It's not necessary for the great benefactor to be at each well in person. It may be that an aide, someone on his staff, looks after these wells for him and sees that water flows freely when certain water-producing processes are met. The water is probably as sweet and abundant as if the author of the well himself were personally present. Also, you must remember that the great benefactor and engineer actually exists and perhaps may be communicated with on justifiable occasions."

"How do we know when we communicate with God?" Mohammed asked.

"I'm not capable of approaching or recognizing the

All Highest," Michael said quietly. "That some personal power at times has answered my prayer I know. I've had personal evidence of such nature that I'd consider myself weak and credulous to call the experience chance or coincidence. I've seen the most unlikely, the one chance in a thousand, come definitely and most naturally to pass."

He paused before continuing.

"On the other hand we mustn't generalize on the specific or declare more than we know. The nature of God is very vast. Those who call the boundary between Him and us the last frontier are simple souls with little conception of the magnitude ahead of man, let alone of the boundless region and mystery of God. However, if believing you communicate direct to the All Highest gives you more power in prayer and life, by all means believe it. No man can say it's not true."

"How should I pray to a personal God, Michael?" R. V. asked.

"I'm not an authority on prayer," Michael said earnestly. "There are others who can tell you a great deal more. But I might make two suggestions. First, reach as high in prayer as you can mentally rise to. I mean, pray to the highest one your evolutionary stage and the intensity of your plea can reach. Such a being would not only be the most understanding but have the most powerful intelligence and energy resources at his command. Secondly, present as humble, honest and eloquent a brief as you can for the justification of your plea. Think out your strong cause and reasons. They have the weight of great energic strength.

"You mean that verse from Isaiah?" Milt asked
quickly. " 'Produce your cause, saith the Lord; bring
forth your strong reasons, saith the King of Jacob.' "

"It couldn't be said better," Michael agreed. "Why
is what you ask important and necessary, not to you
alone but to God? If what you ask won't measure up,
return to yourself and work out such a cause and
promise. If it can't further the spiritual evolution of
others, then of yourself. I mean certain actual things
you can and will do to further your own growth and
understanding. This is throwing your small cause in
with the tremendous cause of the Beyond whose great
business appears to be the inner growth of living beings."

"Whew!" Milt said.

"If not," Michael chided him, "what justification do
you have in wanting to change the plans of the universe? If you have justification, then marshal and
clarify your strong reasons and causes. Not only to
a personal God. It's a powerful factor also to the God
power, principle or presence. Both in God and in ourselves, strong causes and reasons have their effect in
releasing strong energy flows to bathe and resolve our
problems. In fact we can't prove whether we actually
reach up and convince the highest one available to
our stage of progress to use his great energy to accomplish our prayer or whether we only reach in and convince our inner spiritual self, which with its energies
aroused by just cause and reason is somehow through
God's provision able to bring our desire to pass. There
are other possibilities which I won't go into here except to say they are all good."

His words produced a strong effect on us.

"You said there were three chief mental sources. You've given us only one," Milt reminded.

"The other two are more advanced," Michael considered. "Historically old but not so ancient as prayer. The first of these we mentioned once before. We pointed out that most fears of low energy periods have no existence in times of strong energy flow. So in psycho-energics we learn that most things in life are pawns, not real or important in themselves but nuclei for the higher expenditure and energy flows they establish. This is especially true of fear, trouble, mental pain. Now if you can carry on despite the high expenditure of the fear and pain, it might be profitable to your progress to accept the pawns as real and let them build up your system of painful expenditure rates and energy flows."

He paused for a moment, seemed to look at Milt in the darkness, then continued.

"On the other hand, if you're low or ill, if you're a sensitive with such a burden of expenditure already that you can't carry it all and do what's expected of you in the world, you can reject them for what they claim to be."

"What do you mean by reject them?"

"Deny their reality. Declare them pawns, illusions, lies."

We were somewhat startled.

"Won't things come up in your mind to support their reality?"

"They will indeed. You will have to declare mentally that each supporting suggestion is a lie. As they rise, you say, 'That's a lie' and 'That's a lie.' For some time you can expect the organism to keep on making efforts to reintroduce the fear or feared thing in various guises. It does this because it draws energy from the fear's high expenditure while your conscious mind suffers. You may seem to destroy the fear from the front. Sooner or later it will come from the rear. For example, you may deny its existence and then find yourself admitting it by thinking, 'How happy I was before this thing came on me.' Or when you see someone enjoying himself you reflect, 'Once I was happy like he is.' These and a large repertory of such tactics are the technique of the organism to re-establish through stratagem the readmission of the reality of fear in order to resume the robbing of energy through it."

"What can you do about it?"

"You can provide energy to immobilize it by nailing it as a lie. You can even deny that it ever really existed."

"Wouldn't that only beat it back into the subconscious?"

"Many tormented people would be glad to get rid of certain fears, worries and mental suffering out of the conscious where it troubles them and into the subconscious where they can forget them. Don't be afraid of the subconscious. It already carries a great load of shocking things you've forgotten and which would overwhelm a man if they were all suddenly to become conscious and start squandering energy. It can carry a great deal more."

"But how does denial produce results?" Milt asked.

"Denial is an energy release and transfer process, one of the most powerful we have. Its energy flows have been built up by our experience with other lies and frauds, with our indignation for injustice and its suffering, with our history of past denials and with the strength of our particular will. So when we deny, this combination of energy flows applied to the fear resolves its deficit or part of it, releasing energy which helps further to keep it dissolved. The more vigorous and complete the denial, the more energy is raised to dissolve the alleged evil. The more promptly it's denied, the easier to dissolve it. On the other hand, the longer it existed, the greater may be the liberation from additional fears, troubles and ills that have been paying tribute energy to the original fear or suffering. The peculiar value of denial is its design to dissolve completely both the attacked expenditure and itself, not to leave anything in its place as in the case of most other R processes."

"Isn't energy a new concept of denial?"

"Energy is the basis of all things," Michael said. "Never minimize it, or denial either. It's the first weapon of defense, the quickest acting and one of the most complete high-expenditure destroyers I know."

We tried it mentally.

"There was still one more, I think you said," Milt reminded.

"Yes, it's perhaps the most important and advanced of all. Like the last, it also requires work, even harder and more persistent mental work. That's why it's little used. We humans today want our things done for us. In childhood we run to our mother. In prayer we run to God. In sickness, we run to the doctor. In any case, our mother or God or the doctor is appealed to and depended on to take care of our trouble, to fix it up. But in this, like in certain other conscious mental processes, we've got to do it ourselves."

"Isn't that approach old-fashioned today?" Dennis wondered. "In primitive days man had to do everything for himself. Now he harnesses the energy of nature to do it for him and employs a specialist to do the harnessing."

"Yes, and neglects the building of his own energy, the only really important energy that counts," Michael said. "In this particular case, I am the specialist, and the Creator has seen to it that I can only tell you how to do it, not do it for you. A surgeon can go into your nervous system with his instruments and cut out some of your circuits. But he can't rearrange and build up their intricate psycho-energic processes with his hands, and neither can you. To do that he and you must use what cell group and process controls you already have established. Now what strong controls of cell groups and energy flows do you have other than the practise of gratitude and love?"

We were silent a while thinking that out. R. V. spoke first.

"Well, we've found that words release energy. We can say and control words," he suggested.

"Very good. It means we use words to release energy, and we place the words in such order that energy is transferred from strong to needy groups."

We were impressed.

"It's a big order, if you can do it," Dennis said.

"Oh, man's been doing it for a long time, although he wasn't always sure what he was doing."

"What does he call the process?"

"What he practises of it, he calls encouraging himself, bracing himself, talking himself out of something, inspiring himself, affirming faith, and so on. In psycho-energics, we call it a C R or conscious release process. To perform it effectively, we need a mental cell group with powerful energy flows already established so some of this energy can be released and transferred to needy groups. Now what mental conception in most of us is the most powerful?"

"Death," Carl suggested.

"Death is a very powerful group," Michael admitted. "But it's a negative and deficit one. Energy can be transferred from it to great despair and other strong conditions that rival its deficit power. However, in most cases the conception of death is likely to dominate your lesser trouble and suck energy from the needy group instead of releasing energy to it. For general utility we want a positive or surplus group. Now what of our concepts is superior to death?"

"God!" Mohammed cried.

Michael acknowledged it. Mohammed waited in the darkness hungrily, we thought. He was getting his God at last.

"The strong God concept has been building up in man for a long time," Michael pointed out. "It had its greatest growth in the days of the early chieftains and kings. Their power over life and death, their cruelty to their enemies, their grants of wealth, power and title to their friends established tremendous energy expenditure and flows connected with their names. Without kings, especially absolute monarchs, without all the tales of their violence, their gifts and splendor, we could never have come to our mighty conception of God. It set up in our minds under one word a great combination of powerful cell groups. Even in cases when a certain king was good and merciful, the tradition of bloody magnificence supplied an undercurrent of power and energy flow much as the violence, cruelty and self-righteousness of the Old Testament God supplies hidden power and energy flow to the gentler God of the New Testament.

"I can feel the power, Michael!" Mohammed said.

"But there's more to our God concept than that," Michael went on. "The scientists who uncovered vast regions under the microscope and in the telescope added a great deal. Out here in New Mexico we don't need a telescope. Look up!"

We looked. The incomparable Southwestern night sky hung low over us, velvety clear. The infinite blue-black space was strewn with lights ranging from the unwinking planets and bolder stars to the faint swimming specks that made up the Milky Way. Michael went on.

"I think we've spoken before of the millions of galaxies like our Milky Way, each with its billions of suns. All this takes no account of planets which for the most part are too small and dark to be detected. When we consider that most of these suns are greater than our own and that the universe is so vast that the light of many galaxies takes millions of years to reach our small earth, we establish a new and terrific concept of the Creator. The dispatcher or dispatchers of the stars must control energy so immense that our minds are unable to conceive it. This conception of God as the controller of vast new worlds of power and probable life, added to man's earthly conception of the powerful monarch and kind father, gave him a combination of cell groups whose power potential is tremendous and which can be invoked by the single word and thought, God."

"That's true," Carl admitted, "but it's a frightening and weakening thought rather than a strengthening one."

"A negative or energy-deficit God-concept can always be turned into a positive or surplus-energy one," Michael told him. "In fact, the person with a painful deficit God-concept has the greater energy potential. He can employ a number of converters. One is to look behind the ugly face of evil and see the actual laws of good. Another is to change his creed to a belief in God as a benign and loving father. These and other converters dissolve the high expenditure and release energy flow that has been previously consumed by fear, by the threat of eternal hell fire. The one who's been raised to believe in a cruel and vengeful God can often be cured of chronic illness through no more than the energy freed by changing his belief to the complete goodness of God. However, once the new concept of a wholly good God and universe becomes commonplace with him, the energy flows of the old violent God gradually subside. To make use of them again, the total conception must be repeatedly set off and its energy released by a permanent everyday method. This is the rich energy source and release process I'm talking about."

"Just how do you do it?"

"Briefly, you identify your own limited self with the vast unlimited power concept of God," Michael said simply.

We weighed that.

"Can you give us examples?"

"Yes, the ancient Vedas of the Hindus say, 'The quality of the Great One is the same as man.' The Old Testament says in Genesis, 'So God created man in his own image; in the image of God created he him.' Christ put the idea into more practical word form. He said, 'I and the Father are one.' He also urged men to follow him and do as he did, in which case he said they could perform the works that he did. Now if a man dares to follow Christ and identify this tremendous conception of power with himself, certain psycho-energic processes take place. Energy flows are set in motion by man's God-concept. The hungry mouths of the man's deficit cell groups invoked by the pronoun 'I' are also opened at about the same time. The suture words 'and' together with 'are one,' if realized mentally and believed, provide the transfer paths between cell groups. Thus some of the energy of the aroused powerful God groups is absorbed by the activated deficit group of self and identity, strengthening them and giving the declarer an increased sense of well-being and power. The physical machine instantly responds. The man's increased well-being breathes deeper, relaxes, lives and exercises more normally.

We were silent, trying out the words in our mind.

"I say it and don't feel much at all," Carl announced.

"It's very possible," Michael agreed calmly. "It means one of several things. First, your God-concept may be slight. That is, little energy is set off by the word and thought. Or, what is more likely from what you say, your God-concept is on the deficit side, having little energy surplus but rather a deficit to contribute. Also, another factor is likely involved."

"What's that?" Carl asked.

"Your present energy sources already supply your needs. There's an old gibe against religion and goodness and the pure life. It says that most men, even some of the saints, don't turn to God until they've had misfortune or lost the capacity to sin. Of course, this is perfectly normal in psycho-energics. So long as the natural animal processes release enough energy, even those animal processes called sin, perversion, and adultery which are not immoral to most animals, the normal tendency of the organism is to hold to such energy sources. On the other hand, once those animal sources fail or become involved with heavy expenditure so that they begin to yield energy deficits rather than surplus, then suffering or discomfort prods the organism to find other sources in the hope of lowering the deficits."

I couldn't see Carl's face.

"Is that good or bad? I mean to have enough energy resources?"

"Good currently, perhaps not evolutionarily. Trouble hasn't as yet conditioned you to get good results

out of the conscious release process. Trouble invokes
strong energy flows even though high expenditure eats
them up. However, the energy is there, and a strong
C R process word-form can get hold of some. In trouble if you resolve or halt the deficit expenditure momentarily, you release a great deal of energy, bathing
your organism with it. In other words, the time to get
best results from declaring 'I and the Father are one,'
or similar word-forms, is when there are painful circumstances that belie your affirmation."

"That seems extraordinary."

"Well, let's ask R. V. what he felt," Michael suggested. "His handicap should have established some
high expenditure in him. He may even have known
despair at times. I don't know about his God-concept
or a fourth factor we'll get to presently."

We turned our eyes on R. V., who sat very still.
From where I was, he seemed to be under a particularly bright star or planet.

"I felt the power very strong," he said quietly. "In
fact, I'd be grateful for any other energy-releasing
word-forms."

"Religion, psychology and medicine have a good
many," Michael told him. "Some are more effective
than others. Let's look at a popular one of a few years
ago that's not in strong repute today. I mean Dr.
Coué's 'Every day in every way I am getting better
and better.' "

"What happened to it?"

"It became too much of a fad. Also it had several
weaknesses that kept it from surviving. First, its
length, which spread the energy it released over too

many consuming words. Then it didn't declare very much, had a low energy-release aim, which is usually fallen short of in practise anyway. But most of all, it lacked a strong mother cell group to power it with energy. One of our Christian sects does much better. Their affirmations, 'God is my life' and 'Perfect God, perfect man,' remedy these faults. First they use the strong God-concept to power both. In the second place, they aim high, demand a great deal as you can see from the word 'perfect.' In the third place, these two word-forms compress much that's unspoken into them, including the Biblical statement that God created man in His own image. Finally the two word-forms bring in our own needy self group and provide a connection for energy to be transferred to it—all this in four words each."

"If the energy transferred is spread over the whole organism," Milt spoke up, "isn't what reaches the affected part pretty small?"

"At times that's true and foreseen," Michael agreed promptly. "If the affected part is known, energy may be transferred more direct and efficiently to it by bringing the name of the needy part into the word-form. For instance, the second of the above affirmations might be expanded to 'Perfect God, perfect man, perfect eyes.' I include eyes because their unrecognized tension expenditure can deplete and disorganize the nervous system. But any suspect part of us may be used instead."

"What do you mean by perfect?" Dennis asked.

"In the case of God, I mean a higher, greater concept of being, energy and harmony than we know. In

the case of man or part of him, I mean relative per-
fection, a clearing of the organism's nervous system,
bringing a sense of peace and harmony to his particular stage of development, high or low, simple or complex, whatever it may be. We must remember that
strain is always in the cell groups of the psycho-energic nervous system. The words 'pure' and 'perfect' relate to a clearing of this system."

"All we need do then is repeat words?" Carl asked
skeptically.

"Far from it," Michael told him. "But when you
use words, remember those things necessary to power
them. The most important is the God-concept. The
more powerful your God-concept, the richer your
energy source. But there's still another factor that's
the most effective of all when you have it or can develop it."

"What's that?"

"A certain strong, independent energy stream in
addition to that of the God-concept and reinforcing
it. It's a stream that creates itself by resolving the deficit groups of doubt and skepticism and taking over
the energy so released. Can you tell me what it is?"

"It sounds like faith," R. V. suggested.

"Belief," Michael said. "A more active and energy-
rich thing, I think, than faith."

"But belief can be blind, false and even bad!" Carl
protested. "For instance, belief in an evil cause and
leader."

"You mustn't forget that what's believed in is only
a pawn for the energy involved," Michael reminded.
"It's a kind of tag to rate and direct the force attached

to it. It's this energy force of belief that counts primarily, not the object believed in. The power can be transferred from one object to another, converted from bad to good. Belief in questionable objects, gods and men has helped vast numbers of people, actually cured a good many. What a man believes in depends on his mental and spiritual evolution. But at every stage of that evolution, the energy stream of a powerful belief can support him and clear his deficit groups for his well-being. Even though it clears these deficits too easily and he is thus able to reject painful suggestions of scientific truth about himself and thus retard his development, belief remains the most powerful and perhaps the most desired of all energy relief processes."

"What if you don't have belief?" Carl asked.

"There are several things we may do. Repetition helps. Saying an affirmation over and over so fast that it bars skeptical groups from coming in and robbing, keeps the energy trickle going till it may accumulate a volume that dissolves the doubt groups. Declaring the word-form with vigor and force enlarges the stream. Thought and meditation on the meaning and idea of the word-form enlarge and reinforce the cell groups involved and the energy stream released. Living the good life, practising what we preach, makes what good we declare more real and likely to us, releasing increased power and convincing our inner self, which, I suspect, has great power to release vital energies."

"What if you still can't get belief?" Carl asked.

Michael smiled. "Well, you might deny your skepticism, affirm that you actually have belief, and so release energy to construct such a belief."

" 'I believe; help thou mine unbelief!' " Milt quoted.

"Isn't all this the province of religion?" Mohammed asked.

"I'd say that psycho-energics is the common basis of all religion," Michael answered. "It has no watertight compartments. Religious, philosophical and psychological fields are human aspects of the same psycho-energic principles. If you declare, 'God lives, therefore man lives,' it sounds strange to a novice in metaphysics. So does, 'Mother of God' and 'Hail Mary, full of grace, the Lord is with thee' to a non-Catholic. Also, 'There is no God but God and Mohammed is his prophet' to a non-Muslim. So, too, does 'I think, therefore I am,' to a non-philosopher. But all these release energy in persons in whom the practise has established energy flow and perhaps to a lesser extent in all men in whom have been established tolerance, good will and understanding."

Some of us figured it was time to go and stood up, but Milt stayed sitting on the wall curb.

"Isn't there something else the needy sensitive can do?" he persisted.

Michael considered.

"Well, helping others is a strong process of releasing energy to our needy groups. We say it helps us forget our troubles. What happens is that the hardship and misfortune of others sets off high expenditure sympathy groups in us, releasing some energy to our own troubles. Should we mentally and physically help the others, some of this expenditure is resolved, releasing still more energy to our own difficulties."

"What if you don't have enough time for your own troubles, let alone for others?"

"That's a bad spot to think you're in," Michael said gravely. "I don't think it's true but I'll point out a few more energy sources. I suppose what troubles you're chiefly interested in are worry, anxiety, fear, perhaps unhappy memory. Let's look at the strain that sets off these deficit expenditures. I don't mean the original strain that caused them in the first place but the current deficit strain that revives them. The victim will notice that fear or unpleasant remembrance often comes back to mind at the moment when energy is diverted by a sudden or straining action, a turning of the eyes, a disturbing sound, pressure he's put under, suspense, even happiness, anything that calls for extra energy. When this happens, the fear is set off so its energy may be robbed in an effort to have the overdraft relieved. Now what is fear?"

"It implies something bad," Milt suggested.

"Fear is a bad suggestion selected by the imagination for the energy flow. Being quick enough mentally to see the mind take a bad suggestion for its energy content and recognizing it for what it is can be very profitable practise. Nailing it, 'bad suggestion' and 'another bad suggestion,' causes it to lose much of its punch."

"But isn't there something we can do more than just watch and name it as it comes?"

"There is, I think. We can substitute a non-painful energy release process for the painful. Fear very simply is expectation of bad. We know that bad carries energy deficit, inharmony. Good, on the other hand, carries energy surplus or harmony. Therefore the specific for expectation of bad is to change our energy source to its opposite, expectation of good."

"Why doesn't our organism do this automatically?" Milt wanted to know.

"A healthy relaxed organism does," Michael said. "What we have to contend with in the case of an unhealthy tensed organism is the fact that bad expectation carries more energy flow than good. We might say it's a larger pipe line with still larger demands on it, making a deficit, while good expectation is a smaller pipe line with still smaller consumption, providing a surplus. The needy, nervous and excited organism naturally goes after the larger pipe line, disregarding the greater consumption. It also goes after it because the larger pipe line of bad in a tensed organism is active, seldom dormant like the small one of good which is able to relax itself, turn itself off to a trickle."

Michael considered and went on.

"For these reasons, good expectation doesn't occur automatically to the tensed organism which in a bad financial emergency would sooner pick pockets than pick cotton or fruit. Now, picking cotton or fruit is slower and more laborious, but it's far more solidly successful, and we can say the same of the process of good expectation. Each time it's practised, its surplus energy makes less necessary the automatic setting off of bad expectation. Practised persistently, the energy robbing pattern changes. Instead of invoking the bad for energy, the organism starts automatically invoking good expectation. This is what is practised so naturally and pleasantly by the healthy ego type."

He paused for a little before going on.

"There's another leaf the needy sensitive can take out of the healthy ego's book. When the healthy in-sensitive reverts in thought to himself, he usually finds a surplus of energy in his self-group combination. This surplus provides a naturally good opinion of him-self and the feeling that he deserves good. But when the needy sensitive reverts to himself, which is often, he usually finds a deficit of energy in his self-group. This provides a poor opinion of self and a feeling that he deserves bad. Also the sensitive tries at times to re-lieve this self-group deficit by the R process of think-ing he deserves bad for the same psycho-energic reason that a man in despair may punish himself. Such a wasteful R process only increases the energy deficit in the end and must often set off new fear processes for its own relief energy. The antidote is to change the feeling of bad-deserving to good-deserving, to think and tell himself that he deserves good. This is an effi-cient process providing an energy surplus, eliminating the need of setting off fears to relieve it."

"I like that," Milt said.

"In desperate moments, a sensitive can also change the identity of some particularly devastating fear group to a more moderately expending and less ex-hausting group, and consciously fear that instead. I mean, in case a desperate fear is regularly used to sup-ply certain deficits, a lesser fear may be set up as a substitute source or whipping boy, and the organism led to obtain its energy from that, which naturally means less strain and saves a great deal of pain. But something more than this should be aimed for."

"What's that?" Milt asked.

"Deficit cell group subordination known as forgetting. We know that worries and fears are only energy-release processes set off by the organism for energy robbing. Analyzing them too much increases their energy content and makes the organism fight harder to keep using their rich energy sources. As a matter of fact, we never want to work too consciously or hard at any time on our release processes. There is a chance we may start to try to run our body and mind consciously. This is going too far and makes for disorganization. It's imperative to let our far more delicate and expert inner self run through its own intricate sequences. What we should do is stand above, suggesting, declaring, issuing the orders. For instance, we should deny the bad vigorously, tell ourselves with belief that we can control our thought and blot unpleasant things from the mind, and then turn to something else for energy, act as if the unwise release processes didn't exist, and never mention them to anyone else, not even to ourselves except when necessary. In other words, forget them, turn to something else for our energy and act as if they didn't exist."

"It's nice work if you can get it," Milt said. "I liked some of the other things you said. Could you repeat them for me briefly?"

"Deny the fear or worry's reality; repeat and think good imagination, good expectation, good deserving; release energy from what good things you possess;

apply the love stream to every person and thing, especially those persons and things connected with your worry or fear; declare and believe the God presence and power in you; relax physical key tension while poising mentally; increase your fresh air and breathing; and start to forget."

"Thanks, Michael," Milt said, now getting up with alacrity. "I want to make a note of your summary by the car light. Will you come along and straighten me out if I forget anything?"

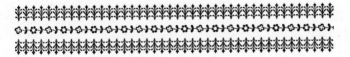

CHAPTER TEN

THE EXPANSION AND CONTRACTION
OF ENERGY EXPENDITURE

*"I will bring the blind by a way that they knew not . . .
I will make darkness light before them, and crooked
things straight."*

ISAIAH *xlii, 16*

SAND STORMS occur most every season in New
Mexico but are more frequent in the spring. The worst
I ever saw came in June. It lasted three days and two
nights. Another that I knew in June chased the gradu-
ating exercises indoors from the university campus.

Now in early summer it was blowing again. Little
dust reached us at Sandia Park, high as we were and
protected by the mountains. But far to the east and
below us I could see great brown clouds racing over
the Estancia Plain and rising to thousands of feet.

It would be worse around Albuquerque and across
the east mesa, I knew. No paved highway ran through
Tijeras Canyon then, only a narrow sandy road along
the arroyo. As a result I didn't expect the boys today.
But when I reached San Antonito, Carl's car stood outside of Michael's door. The Faithful Five were waiting
inside. A new, partly finished rug of Indian design
hung on the loom. The boys were discussing and ad-
miring it when I came in.

Michael stood by, pleased with their praise.

"You see a rug," he said. "It looks very simple. But if you unravel it, you find how much of somebody's mind and hands went into it. So a psycho-energist looking at the energy patterns of life finds how much of a creator's thought must have gone into it."

"You're assuming there was a creator?" Carl suggested.

"No, what I'm doing is not assuming there wasn't any. Assuming is a primitive characteristic. I remember in Sparta seeing Grecian columns, very old, covered with moss, almost buried in the ground. The goats for centuries, I suspect, assumed they were a normal condition of nature, like rocks from a cliff. Then an anthropologist came along and recognized them as the work of a human mind. But they had been the work of a mind all the time."

"Some scientists don't believe in God," Carl declared.

Michael heard him mildly.

"Carl, you say that as if God didn't believe in God. I've known a good many scientists, some better than others, and can assure you that they're not much different from other people. Especially in their personal habits and beliefs. You mustn't take scientists' personal feelings for science."

"Why don't scientists believe in God?" Mohammed asked.

"Many do. Those that don't have normal human reasons like other people. For one thing, it's sometimes difficult for an ego with a strong inquiring mind to admit there's a being or beings so infinitely far above him and his associates in intelligence that he's only a mite beside them. The opposite feeling, that he and his associates for the first time since the world began are charting intelligent paths through a blind and helpless universe, is a strong R process releasing energy to the scientist's life and work. To admit that his cherished discoveries are only the finding of colored eggs hidden by the Creator in a kind of cosmic children's Easter hunt would cut him off from some of his richest energy sources."

"I can understand that," Dennis said. "I've felt it myself sometimes."

"We must also remember that skepticism is a native quality of the scientist," Michael pointed out. "He wouldn't be a scientist without doubting, analyzing, and checking. Not to be tied down to any particular religion, he feels, makes him stronger in his own right and his reputation so among other scientists. He's aware that his brother scientists aren't as loving and forgiving as their Christian brothers toward what they consider sinners and backsliders. However, sometimes the skeptic leans so far backward that he predicates his work on nature without the possibility of a Creator. After a while he finds he's on a one-way street. All phenomena he examines have to be interpreted from this point of view. If anything contradicts it, the evidence must be edited to conform or else outright rejected."

Michael considered and went on.

"Some scientists' private lives and behaviour patterns affect their beliefs like those of other men. They may have personal reasons for preferring a philosophy without God. To deny Him, they feel, allows more moral freedom. To admit Him might give their conduct and morals painful problems. Then there are men in all professions who seem incapable of recognizing or appreciating a Creator as some men lack the faculty of recognizing or appreciating art or music. Finally, I've known inquiring minds whose observation of evil made them conscientiously doubt the existence of God. When they find facts or explanations that convince them otherwise, I'm sure they'll just as conscientiously change their position."

"How can you be sure?"

"Well, I was such a one myself," Michael confessed.

"What converted you?"

"I wasn't converted in the usual emotional sense. An emotional conversion is a type of R process. A torrent of energy released by promised salvation from cruel religious or other fears resolves and relaxes all doubt. Now a thinking man, as a rule, doesn't have a great mass of religious fears to release a torrent of energy from. His conversion involves the same process and the same kind of energy, but in sections, piecemeal. One energy flow released by the solution of a problem, resolves certain doubts. Another resolves others and so adds up gradually. However, some doubts or problems still remain or recur, and the thinker sets his mind to resolve these by fair means if possible; if not, to let them stand. This means that a problem like the existence of God is never proven absolutely a hundred percent. The evidence is fifty, sixty, seventy or ninety percent. Even Christ cried out, 'My God, my God, why hast thou forsaken me?' "

"Isn't that bad?" Mohammed asked.

"To a thinker or scientist? No. I'd say it's good. The moment he's a hundred percent sure of his knowledge of something, his usefulness in the subject as a scientist may be questioned, his exploration suffers and his new findings grow one-sided."

"But shouldn't he admit God?" Mohammed persisted.

"The Creator Himself is a very retiring and self-effacing being," Michael said thoughtfully. "It's not easy to prove him to a man who derives energy from believing in the superiority of himself over the God idea. The same goes for disproving God to one who derives supporting energy from belief in God's existence. In either case it may not be necessary. In both men psycho-energic growth goes on just the same. You know, the rain falls on the just and the unjust. It's this inner growth that counts and not the creed, skepticism or arguments for either."

"You say, inner growth. Can you tell us what you mean?"

"Its chief method that I've observed appears to be something we talked about before—the expansion and contraction of energy expenditure. We especially talked about the contraction part of it, remember? In reality, the expansion part of the E C E is the more important. When expansion occurs, it establishes in the nervous system a new higher rate, a greater volume or longer duration of expenditure than before. Once established, this becomes normal, a natural possession or equipment of the organism, and can be set off again. Now our concept of the Creator is of a being of infinite power not only in energy resources but in the scale and sensitivity of His energy spending. Therefore a process that establishes a higher scale of sensitivity and greater volume or rate of power in us, we might loosely call a process of creative growth, for it tends to make us more like our Creator."

We had pricked up our ears.

"Can you show us this process, Michael?" Mohammed asked.

"I must caution you first," Michael said. "Expansion of expenditure to new rates and broader volumes of energy flow means deficit, pain, suffering for a time. As a result, such expansion is unpopular, against the organism's will. Today the Western world calls much of this process evil. Modern progress and science do their best to conquer it. They're confounded when it springs up more powerful and to most people more terrible than before in the very ashes where they thought they had destroyed it. What they don't realize is that it is apparently an integral process of the Creator and that the cards are stacked against those who try to destroy it. For example, when and if we overcome war and its increasing terrors, we'll find there are other obstructive forms of the creative process waiting for us, such as the stupidity of popular leaders and the selfish weakness of popular majorities. When we overcome disease and lengthen life, we'll run into new problems such as over-population and starvation."

"I wouldn't call growth toward God evil, Michael!" Mohammed protested.

Michael looked at him, then at us.

"How about a little trip today?"

"In weather like this!" several of us protested.

"You see?" Michael said enigmatically. "Even youth today shuns expansion of expenditure. It's a sign of the times. It wasn't so when I was a boy."

When we left the house, we found that the storm had risen. Dust was flying now in San Antonito. The summit of the Sandias looked hazy but we knew the illusion came from a lower layer of dust we had to look through. At eleven thousand feet altitude, the air should be clear and pure. A forestry road ran to the summit and several of us had a notion Michael wanted to take us there. To our disappointment he suggested driving down into Tijeras Canyon.

Gradually as we dropped to a lower altitude, we entered the level of the storm fury. Soon we were surrounded by clouds of dust lifted and propelled by strong winds. There were times when I had to stop the car and wait until I could see. Although midmorning, it seemed late afternoon. Showers of sand with occasional small pebbles kept striking the car body and windshield. The mountain heights to the right of the canyon had melted away. We saw no one on horse or foot and only a single car.

Coming out of the canyon we were met by still stronger winds of the open mesa. Swirling yellow currents of sand and dust advanced up the road toward us, attacking the car, shutting it in and pouring fine siftings through the cracks. The road seemed at a dead end, a few feet of dirt leading from nowhere to nowhere. Everything else had disappeared.

Michael rode with me peering through the windshield with owlish intensity. Suddenly he told me to turn left on a pair of wheel tracks. In a few minutes we seemed completely lost.

"I hope you know where you're going," I said.

"We're going to see my friend, Dominguez," he told me. "That is, if he's home, and he should be in this weather."

We passed over a cattle guard and dropped down into a cañada. Presently an adobe ranch building loomed out of the storm. When we stepped out of the car we could see ranch house walls as massive as a fortress. An old Mexican woman with a black rebozo pulled over her head let us in the heavy patio gate.

One minute we had been in the fury of the storm. The next we stood in a quiet spartan room behind thick earthen walls with few windows. There were rude settees and chairs with rawhide seats. A few coals of pinyon wood glowed in the rounded earthen fireplace in the corner. The Mexican woman asked us to sit down. Her brother had gone to visit the next ranch but she'd send for him.

"You said you'd show us the E C E process," Dennis reminded when she was gone.

Michael smiled.

"Didn't you see it?"

We looked at each other. Michael went on.

"We might point out roughly that there are two kinds of energy deficiency. One is caused by the lowering of flow available to usual energy requirements. We grow tired, need sleep and food, grow old and so on. The other kind of deficiency is caused by unusual energy requirement. We run into disappointment, a problem to solve, a thorn to pull out, a chasm to jump, an enemy to fight, many kinds of shock. The ride down here today was one of unusual energy requirement."

"Go on," we told him.

"Above-normal expenditure was set off by the sand storm through our eyes, our ears, our breathing, through the possibility of getting lost or having an accident, through absence of reality and familiar landmarks without the substitution of new ones. Having little experience with sand storms, no expenditure in the past had built up sufficient energy flows to these special conditions in ourselves. As a result the deficits were considerable and painful. However, sooner or later the thorn is pulled, the chasm is jumped, the enemy is routed. A few minutes ago when we entered this house, we suddenly came to peace and quiet. Our eyes and ears and throats were freed from attack. Our minds were no longer troubled by uncertainty, by the fear of being lost. We found ourselves surrounded by real landmarks of a more or less familiar life pattern. Although high expenditure stopped, our aroused energy flows don't stop so suddenly. Too inadequate to reduce pain much during storm expenditure, they are now with greatly lowered expenditure enough to provide a small surplus. For a time while we enjoy that boon, a margin of available energy flows over expenditure. We call it relief, relaxation, enjoyment, peace, contentment. Don't you feel it?"

Smilingly we agreed.

"Even I feel it, Michael," R. V. said.

"But stay here long enough," Michael promised, "and those energy flows will subside, too. Already

yours have probably gone down a little. The sensation of relief and peace isn't quite so deep and sweet
as when we first came. Am I right?"

We had to admit that what he said was true. He
went on.

"Eventually, if you stayed, these walls that look so
protective, peaceful and pleasant to you would lose
their charm. They'd no longer have energy flow available for the cell groups sensing them through the eye.
You'd say then you were getting a little restless or
had enough of it and would have to go. It's our way
of expressing that our energy flows are down and
we're ready for other processes to arouse them."

A rain of sand struck the small window.

"My enjoyment in the place hasn't gone down yet,"
Dennis remarked.

"Not so long as the storm keeps on invoking energy
flow to your involved cell groups," Michael agreed.
"You don't need to see or hear it. You need only to
realize it. You remember that any haven is sweet so
long as the memory of outside difficulties, to which
we're immune in the refuge, keeps releasing energy
flow to it."

"Then the beauty felt in relief from violence in music and art is an E C E process?"

"Yes, enjoyment of beauty is through energy released by the contraction part of the E C E process.
It may be an original E C E or a revival. Often in
the revived E C E, the conditions that caused the strain
in the first place no longer apply and we feel only the
pleasant energy released by contracted expenditure.
It's therefore as a rule not the revived E C E that we

dislike, dread, take every means to avoid, but the original establishment of painful expenditure expansion."

Michael looked around at us closely to see if we understood, then went on.

"This wasn't always true. People of the older days had by virtue of their philosophy a greater value and respect for the establishment of expanded expenditure, however painful. Most every boy and girl were subjected to it for their own good. It was called training, discipline, hardening, Proverbs illustrating it were common. Spare the rod and spoil the child. Some races said, hate the child and spare the rod. A child slow to learn to swim might be thrown into deep water where it would have to swim or sink. A boy or man was seldom offered help, however heavy his task, unless he asked for it. The older generation believed that in time the boy would build up his own mental, physical and moral energies. Today we with our weaker flows are anxious for our children to have comfortable rate-flows, the only ones we can understand. We believe the rigor of older times to have been cruel, carried much too far. We think the same of the Creator's expanded expenditure projects in our behalf, which we call misfortune, adversity, evil, things we can't understand. On the other hand, older generations often accepted these things as the wise dispensation or discipline of the gods."

"I'm surprised to hear you support the good old days," Carl said. "History shows they had little refinement, schooling or invention, but plenty of hard labor, discomfort and hardship."

"That's what made them the good old days to those who called them that," Michael answered patiently. "The greater the difficulties of the pioneer, the more did his hardship, insecurity, danger and discomfort establish strong energy flows in him so that when resolved by hope in and effort toward eventual victory over them, the released energy of these hardships gave pleasure, not pain. The idea of pain wasn't in the pioneer so much as in modern people with fainter energy flows who look back on the pioneer and invent tales of his suffering and despair to cut him down more to their own size. They can never understand his satisfaction and even pleasure in his lot, as a hand-fed-and-housed parrot taken aloft in an airplane can never understand the preference and satisfaction of the eagle flying up there alone under his own pioneered power."

"Can you give us other examples of the establishment of expanded expenditure?" Dennis asked with respect.

"Yes, you may be calloused or indifferent to the plight of the poor and needy. However, if you become poor yourself and go through the ordeal of poverty and want, expanded expenditure connected with the poverty will be established in you. Hereafter when you come in contact with the poor and needy, rate-flows of this painful expanded expenditure will be set off in you. The painful high expenditure of others has now been transferred to your own psycho-energic system, and you relieve this deficit in yourself by helping out the others as you can."

"Why must a man experience poverty hardship

himself to be kind to the poor and needy?" Milt asked. "Why can't we teach him charity and kindness?"

"Ah, yes, the panacea of modern education," Michael said cheerfully. "Education as practised today is part of the cult of comfort—an attempt to get around the pain of the universal process of expanded expenditure. Moderns shrink from what their grandfathers went through. So they set up the proposition that charity, tolerance, kindness, generosity and other virtues can be established in the human being by instruction, propaganda, repetition. As a hopeful and soft-hearted human being I'm in great sympathy with the movement and try to practise it even though I'm often confounded by the results. Also, as an observing psycho-energist, disturbing questions confront me. Surely these easier methods were available to the Creative Engineers ages ago. Why then, if these easier methods produce the same results, were the people of centuries ago put through torment and hardship? Was ancient man so stupid that he couldn't have been instructed, while modern man is so intelligent that he may be? History teaches us nothing of the sort."

"Perhaps man's discovered some new means of evolution that God didn't know," Carl said.

Michael looked at him benignly.

"You see what I meant a little while ago when I spoke of the ego that feels itself superior to the Creator. The conclusion of a psycho-energist must be that the universe doesn't lack instructors or means of instruction. Rather he feels that the permanent inner results of education still remain to be seen. Being taught something is not experiencing it. Little or no expanded rates are built into the pupil. He doesn't finally do things because of established psycho-energic processes that have become a deep part of him. He has simply learned, memorized, been taught to practise certain easy virtues like a dog is taught to put his paws in front of his eyes to pray. It looks the same but what goes on inside is quite different. The growth has been slight, superficial. Let a change come in government, instruction, or propaganda, and the people who have learned one set of beliefs by education now learn as easily something else, perhaps the exact opposite. There has been no creative growth in their inner psycho-energic substance, only in their outside habits."

"Then why do you teach us, Michael?" Milt asked.

"I teach you because you came to me and asked questions," Michael answered with dignity. "My opinion of the Creator's compassion, intelligence and inventiveness is too great to let me suspect that I must come and instruct you or you will be lost somewhere on the way. Perhaps I can show you wiser and shorter cuts to take, but there are a great many roads to God, and none of them are actually dependent on me or on you, only on Him and His processes. What I've seen of the Creator's work teaches me that none of us can outwit or elude Him. None of us, even the worst or most obscure, are forgotten in the scheme of creative growth. Some of us may hold off that growth and the painful expansion of its rate-flows for a while. In this event the Creator pityingly compensates our failure to gain the priceless riches of growth by soothing us with small pleasures or content, like a compassionate parent compensates with toys and playthings a retarded child who fails to grow up to the privileges of adult intelligence and being."

"Most people would rather be retarded psycho-energically and have the compensation rather than to grow," R. V. observed.

"Very true," Michael agreed. "We had a simple-minded man in our town who considered himself more fortunate than other men. They were the simple-minded ones to him because they had to work and he didn't. The great rewards of psycho-energic growth have to be reached to be appreciated. It's hard for one caught in the toils and torment of some stage of expanded expenditure to know what's happening to him, to appreciate it and take heart."

"Is there nothing he can do for himself?" R. V. persisted.

Michael was silent for a time.

"There are, of course, a number of things. I've spoken of a few but will mention one of them again. You remember that the business of the universe appears to be the creative growth of man and probably of all life. This growth we know is accomplished by the establishment of expanded rate-flows and their accompanying technical factors. Now the expanded rate-flows in turn are brought on by problems, hardship, obstruction, trouble, which in turn are brought on much by natural causes and events, by what we might call fate, destiny. You know the restraining control of wise parents on children often slackens when they see the child taking hold of his own education and able to take care of himself. Well, a man by taking hold of his own creative growth seems at times to re-move himself from the stratagems of destiny estab-lished in his evolutionary behalf. Such a course may even bypass some of the harsher blows slated by fate or by the inevitable consequences of a weaker course. It may be that when one is far enough, the certain kinds of hardship, adversity and evil that we know here are unnecessary and may be said not to exist, much as sea problems such as sinking, drowning and sharks no longer apply on reaching land where one is free to lie down and rest for a time on the beach be-fore tackling the higher problems of land. I don't ac-tually know about this. I'm only speculating. What I have become much more convinced of is that the powers-that-be appear to recognize an individual's honest and intelligent efforts at creative self-growth and often let him have some respite from fate to see what he can do with himself."

"How does the individual assume his own creative growth?"

"One way long known and practised is self-disci-pline. Self-discipline is simply the self-administering of hardship which is otherwise administered by fate and the nature of things. To the individual it has the advantage of personal choice in the matter of hard-ship. To the universe it has the advantage of graduat-ing a student to a higher and more intelligent method of growth. Indeed, self-administering of hardship doesn't bring only spiritual but material results."

"Can you give us examples?"

"Well, a classic example is the legend of Demos-thenes learning to overcome stuttering by practising speech with his mouth full of pebbles. I've heard a modern speech specialist refer to this with contempt. Certainly there are more comfortable methods to overcome stuttering today, and this is the age of comfort. But the legend is sound psycho-energically. The effort and struggle to speak with the difficulty of a mouth full of pebbles would establish expanded expenditure to the mouth so that when the pebbles were removed, more energy rate-flows had been provided to be released to the speech muscles and the mental groups governing them. The same principle is practised in running with a weight, then discarding the weight, making one feel light-footed."

"Are there any other examples?"

"Yes, I think so. The training and discipline of athletes and of our armed forces. The long mental and financial ordeal of a student preparing for medicine. The trials of a man I know who started his business career not in good times but during the handicaps of a depression. After that, ordinary times seemed rich and easy to him. The sacrifices of parents, of practical missionaries like Dr. Schweitzer, of many who take on burdens for others. These are all more or less self-administered projects of expanded energy expenditure. Non-self-administered E C E is also common, such as storm and clearing, night and day, confinement and liberation."

"You mean a person is better if he's confined to prison?" Carl grinned.

"Gandhi would have probably said so in his case. Not all of us can go to jail, but most of us at one time or another are confined to bed, hospitals, homes and other places. Enforced confinement in school, church, factory and hospital expands energy expenditure, releasing energy for enjoying nature and outdoors. This is also true of confinement in the home especially if there's trouble, friction or unhappiness. The unhappy one looks out to where the difficulty doesn't prevail. Trouble energy is released to objects out there. As a result, nature takes on increased beauty and interest."

"I can't believe that hardship would advance us," Milt said.

"It's not always easy to see," Michael agreed. "Many forms of E C E are complicated. Let's look at one that fathers philanthropy and public service. A man loses a favorite son in war, accident or disease. The greater our youth's promise and more tragic the circumstances, the heavier is the expansion of energy expenditure in his parent. Now the parent's painful energy deficits are centered in those cell groups of his representing the loss of the boy. It seems impossible to relieve them without reproducing the live boy. But the father may be instinctively led to supply energy to these starved groups by a conscious relief process in the form of a trust or memorial or some public service. To do any good to the parent, energy must be released and transferred in him from his active project groups to his painful deficit son groups. This is accomplished by naming the trust or memorial after the boy or perhaps only by the secret resolve or knowledge that the man is doing it for the son and his memory. This is the transfer point of energy between the two groups in the parent and is why he will often keep repeating the boy's name with the subject. If the memorial is a library or scholarship where the service is continuous, the furnishing of energy to the painful deficit groups is more continuous. Should the project be of benefit to boys, energy is more efficiently transferred in the parent from his cell groups representing live boys to those representing the dead one, for these two boy groups have overlapping identity in his system."

"Then the E C E is pretty important to man?"

"The E C E isn't confined to man. It operates in animals and insects as well. Those of us who live at this altitude know the prevalence of moths during the summer season. Many evenings I release a number of them, sometimes twenty or more. They find their way in the house and are drawn to the windows when it begins to get dark. Now if I release them at once when they come out of hiding, their flight as a rule is ordinary. But if I have been away and come home later and find them still struggling at the windows, the effect is different. For an hour or more, the moth has been beating its wings against the glass or screen, tracking it up and down endlessly trying to find a way through. You'd think this ordeal would lower the energy flow. But expanded expenditure has established more flow. When I take the moth to the door and toss it out, it soars to freedom with such a burst of released energy that often it rises above the house."

"I'm amazed, Michael," Mohammed said. "I had no idea."

"Not only animals and insects, but I suspect that plants are subject to the same process," Michael went on. "I remember one winter when I worked in New York State. It was the most severe for many years. It would kill the flowers for next year, I thought. It did kill some plants. But next spring and summer both the tame and wild flowers that survived were the most luxuriant anyone remembered. The horticulturists explained it by saying the intense cold and ice had killed off the natural insect and bacteria enemies of the plants. But that didn't explain how dogwood flowers in New Jersey could be twice as large as I had ever seen them and some others in proportion. There must be something vital affected in the plant or tree itself, I felt. Now I suspect it was the long, severe and unbroken cold that by resistance and oppression developed and stimulated the strength and vitality of the life energy. Once this resistance was released by spring, the plant's stepped-up life force flowed and soared like it did in the moths from my window."

"What I don't like is the thesis of the E C E process —that God causes evil," Carl said.

"You're not unusual in that," Michael considered soberly. "The axe that's being ground is seldom pleased, however necessary the purpose. Our ancestors were upset and outraged when the sexual character of plants was discovered. They felt that God would never stoop to that. Savages feel bitter and even homicidal toward hospital attendants when they see a member of their tribe carried into the operating room, put under an anesthetic and seemingly attacked with a surgeon's knife. The child resents old-fashioned parents who make him stay indoors and study his difficult lessons when it would be far more pleasant to go out and play."

"Some modern educators support the child," Milt mentioned.

"Only the naive and immature see virtue in eliminating the adverse conditions that brought man to where he is," Michael commented. "Permanent release from the E C E process wouldn't mean harmony but stagnation. For harmony you need the freshly renewed energy flows of constant E C E processes."

"Thoreau observed that, I think," R. V. mentioned. "He wrote, 'There's no serenity so fair as that which is just established in a tearful eye.' "

"Excellent. The tear is a symbol and evidence of the painful expenditure now suddenly relaxed, releasing energy flow to the eye, establishing a surplus state easily recognized. Once we understand these psychoenergic facts, under no circumstance would we want to wipe out man's difficulties. Without the strain processes, there could be no constant supplies of energy flows available, and man would probably try to get energy by excitation through unwise and often desperate R processes."

"Pain is still evil to me," Carl persisted.

"Yes, the illusion of evil is very real to many of us lacking the required energy flow in the right places and resentful of the universe's eternal efforts to establish it there," Michael admitted. "But we must understand that, given surplus energy to the cell groups representing the problem, there's actually no evil, only pleasure and stimulation. The mountain peaks that frighten the novice climber are only a challenge to the hardy expert. It's like dangerous surf to the robust swimmer and death to the hero. I suspect it's the way we and our most desperate problems look to the Creator and powers-that-be. Of course, they know the unreality of our problems. But some of us do too and are still affected by their illusion. On the other hand, the Creator, having abundant energy to meet and resolve the high expenditure rates set off by observing our small burdens, feels no sense of fear, pain, calamity or evil for us and as a consequence no compulsion to rush to our aid. It's the psycho-energic explanation of the verse from Habakkuk that God is 'of purer eyes than to behold evil.' "

"I think your expansion and contraction of energy lets me understand things I didn't before," Dennis said.

"The E C E principle is at the heart of many puzzling life questions," Michael agreed. "Why is something good at one time and not at another? For example, rest. When it's the contraction part of the E C E, rest feels good because of the energy flows aroused by the preceding expansion of expenditure. On the other hand, when there's been no such expansion beforehand, no energy flows have been stirred up by long activity or difficulty to be released and harvested by contraction. Then rest may be a bore. People who don't work very hard physically smile at the idea of a laborer content to sit on a chair on a porch. If sedentary workers toiled in the wheat field or woods from sunup to sundown, they'd find the same pleasure in simply contracting the expenditure and basking in its continuing energy flows."

He looked at us closely and went on.

"We must keep in mind also that the expansion part of a process may have taken place before we observed it. If we examine our changing tastes we find that during the last century, Americans worked extremely hard, met great physical difficulties, toiled long hours. They had so much expenditure expansion in their lives that to look at a simple, peaceful work of art or listen to a sweet, quiet piece of music acted as expenditure contraction and harvested the energy flows already aroused in them. Today Americans sit at desks or stand at assembly lines or ride in cars and school busses so that energy flows must be aroused for art and music, which explains in part the rise of violence in art and dissonance in music."

"You said once that easy times, pleasures and security mean weaker energy flows, weaker people, weaker memories. Doesn't this weaken the country?" R. V. asked.

"Barbarians who keep their hardship and energy flows through ignorance nearly always overrun civilized races who discard their hardship and practise refinement with supposed vision," Michael said gravely.

We were silent.

"What country do you expect to overrun us?" Carl asked.

"The answer, of course, is that I don't know," Michael answered. "I'm not a prophet, only an observer. On the one hand, I observe the Creator building up, strengthening the energy flows of man. On the other hand, I see political leaders of democratic countries strengthening armaments while at the same time they weaken man's energy flows in the name of progress.

A psycho-energist doesn't need to be a prophet to see what's begging to happen. He might even predict the character of countries to overrun the countries of more popular will."

"Tell us, Michael!" Mohammed urged.

"Well, first they are likely to be countries whose leaders either by indifference or design refrain from weakening the organic and moral energy of their people with luxury, comforts, security, abundance. Instead and perhaps intentionally, they would be nations that build and keep up the energy flows of its people with certain discipline and repression, often hard times and hard lines. I would also expect such countries to be from the North."

"Why the North?"

"Well, the North supplies one hardship that man has never completely tamed. I mean winter, snow, ice and cold. All other things being equal, men disciplined by winter the greater part of the year may be expected to have more enduring energy flows than men of the milder zones."

"Couldn't countries of popular will be saved from disaster?" R. V. asked.

"Ah, yes," Michael said sadly. "Their energy flows could be built up but seldom are. It means too much discomfort. And yet, if there's another way to provide us with strong enduring energy flows, the Creator doesn't seem to practise it on this planet. Nations are strengthened and saved from the fatal softness and refinements of degeneration by the same process as individuals are, by the painful practise of expanded energy expenditure. We know that in countries of popular will, the enactment of such an important course isn't left to the judgment of their wisest men but to the will of all the people, most of whom don't like the painful expansion of energy expenditure but only its pleasant contraction. This is the Achilles heel of all countries of popular will. If the choice of evolution and its hardships had been left to the vote of our ancestral monkeys, we would still have tails. Democratic man is resolved to stay ease-loving man as long as possible. But we should remember that whatever the universe's form of government, it's not that of popular will. There's no vote taken among us whether we wish to be born or die or suffer here on this planet."

"Is there nothing we can do?"

"Individually, yes. Nationally, it's much harder. The consequences of weakness, which are hardship administered from without, can be forestalled only by energy flows established by hardship administered from within. The pity is the tragically small chance countries of popular will have to take advantage of it. A few wise leaders may be converted to hardship and self-denial for themselves. Once the practise is forced on the people, the leaders would soon be out of office. In their places would be elected candidates promising ease, security, and plenty in some scheme guaranteed to get around the laws of the universe. Toward the end of a nation's life when hardship from without is finally in control, even an ease-loving popular majority can see the handwriting on the wall. But then as a rule it's too late in the game for inner discipline to accomplish anything. The fateful hour has passed."

We talked for a long time but Dominguez didn't

appear. Word came that when last seen he had ridden on to Hell Canyon to look after some cattle. Upon hearing this, we left and were directed on what was said to be a shorter road to the Tijeras Canyon road. It turned out to be longer and extraordinarily rough. When we came to the scraped state highway, R. V., who was riding in the car with us, remarked how smooth and velvety the road felt.

"The road hasn't changed any since we traveled on it a couple of hours ago," Michael pointed out. "Only you have. The hardship and insecurity of the rough road a minute ago stirred up energy flows to your cell groups affected by riding. When we got to the main highway, the expanded expenditure stopped and the released energy flows now cushion the road for you. When in a few minutes those flows die down, the smoothness will die out too."

"Will you say that again, Michael?" R. V. requested.

"I'll say it another way," Michael obliged. "Simple nonexistence of pain isn't sweet in itself. It's only when some E C E process has released energy to the cell groups in question that the lack of pain becomes delectable. So the harmony of today is the direct product of the inharmony of yesterday. The Creator's purpose appears to be the raising of our expenditure rates and energy flows for our increased power and our appreciation of good and beauty, the multiplication of our groups to give us wider experience and understanding, and the establishment of more transfer points to enable us to resolve our own deficit problems."

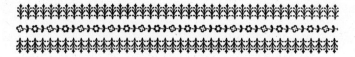

CHAPTER ELEVEN

THE GREAT MISSING
PSYCHO–ENERGIC PROCESS

"Yol bolsum!" (*"May there be a road!"*)
TURKI GREETING TO PILGRIMS IN THE DESERT

THE FINAL semester at the university was over. I knew that Milt had planned to go back East, that R. V. was leaving for his home in Missouri and that Dennis had a job with the Santa Rita Mining Company. Indeed I thought they had already gone. Sunday morning it was raining in the mountains, and when I called at Michael's house, he said he had seen no one. Later in the afternoon Carl came for me, and I found that the others had stayed over for a few days. We were to be together once more. Mohammed was at Michael's house, too. Pakistan, he said, was too far for a college vacation, and Carl had taken a cabin in the Cedar Crest country.

R. V. was speaking to Michael as we came in.

"All week I've been thinking about your E C E process. I'd like to ask you something. What's the use of all this increased energy and energy control established by pain and hardship if the man or animal doesn't live?"

"Ah," Michael nodded. "That's the question I ask myself. I don't know the answer. I can only speculate."

"Will you speculate for us?" R. V. asked.

"Well," Michael considered gravely, "to make use of the increased energy facilities that E C E gives us, something like survival is indicated."

"You mean survival of the race?" Carl put in. "The drops of water die but the wave lives on."

"Most expenditure-expanding processes including death should be beneficial to the race," Michael answered. "But I didn't mean that. The drops of water in your analogy aren't living organisms subject to the E C E process. Neither do they always die before the wave. No, I don't think that all the intense and intelligent psycho-energic care lavished on the living individual for improvement of his energy equipment can be explained by race survival. The most outstanding, gifted and evolved individuals of a race, such as Abraham Lincoln for instance, seldom breed their kind. Races decline and die, too, transmitting only their knowledge and pride and physical qualities rather than their higher spiritual qualities to their descendants. The only answer that makes sense of the psycho-energic processes seems to be individual survival."

"If survival is true, why don't we know about it?" Milt asked.

"Some claim they do," Michael said. "Unfortunately, when we examine the evidence, we find it isn't reproducible for observation and check, as is, for example, the evidence of the chemist or inventor. Some say that survival must be taken on faith. But, as Carl pointed out, man has faith at times in the false as well as the true."

"You mean survival can never be proved?"

"No, I don't mean that. There's always the chance that man may be able to do tomorrow what he can't today. Meantime in the absence of direct and positive proof, we must fall back on what circumstantial evidence we have."

"Well, the strongest evidence we have is that no man ever returned from the grave," Carl said.

"You somewhat exaggerate and over-simplify," Michael reflected. "Generally speaking it's true enough and is, as you say, strong evidence. On the other hand, this strong evidence for oblivion may also be used on the other side of the argument—for survival."

"How could you do that?" Carl looked incredulous.

"Well, let's examine it in the light of our psycho-energic understanding. Whether or not we live on to make any use of its benefits afterward, we know that death is the most powerful and effective of our common E C E processes. Sickness and accident are lesser ordeals. There's always the hope of recovery. But death is final, irrevocable. I know of no other such potent expander of expenditure and energy flow both in the individual facing death and in those suffering his loss."

Michael hitched himself forward on his bench and went on.

"Now if death turns out to be what, among other things, it may possibly be, a top E C E process designed for expanding the scale of the surviving energy instrument, then silence from the grave, the inability to produce survival evidence and the muddling of what little communication seems to seep through could also be design, by the same mind that invented the psycho-energic processes, and for a perfectly understandable reason. For example, clear and evidential communication proving that the dead still lived would kill death's power as an effective E C E process for establishing higher rates and flows. It would make dying little more than a trip to a foreign country, and bedside attendance at death much like seeing a friend off at the pier."

"Why should God bother to give survival to man?" Milt asked.

"Why should He have established psycho-energic processes that give us a higher scale of intelligence and energy in the first place? There's a small significant piece of evidence to look at here. We know the more brutal a man, the less he cares about human life and the more he destroys it for his own ends. On the other hand, the higher his state that's generally called spiritual, the more compassionate he is for other men's lives and the more passionate to share his own substance in their welfare. From this we may infer that the sharing of one's substance for the welfare of others is a characteristic of what is called spirit, increasing in intensity and intelligence as the spiritual scale rises. If this is so, we should count as normal the desire of the Creator to share with man his own substance, including survival."

"What's the strongest circumstantial evidence you know for survival, Michael?" R. V. asked.

"There's a great deal to choose from," Michael answered thoughtfully. "What I call strong might not appear so at all to you, perhaps not even evidence. It depends on our individual make-up and experience.

You may be impressed by the fact that all over the world, especially in the old days when transmission of ideas from country to country was limited, a common pattern of survival testimony and its peculiarly characteristic details appeared in alleged communications in widely separated places and times, even among untaught children whose parents promptly disavowed them. On the other hand, you might be more interested by personal incidents such as abound in the British and American annals of psychic research. I remember one small significant passage where an alleged communicator interjected the word 'milk' to change a medium's persistent rendering of the word 'Bunny,' which was wrong, to 'Bossy,' a calf, which was apparently right. Although it didn't conclusively prove anything, it pointed to an active communicating mind and purpose rather than the dream world of the subliminal."

"How about circumstantial evidence?" R. V. persisted.

"Of course, you know I'm interested in engineering," Michael said. "Well, there's a bit of circumstantial evidence that happens to appeal to me personally. Let's say a shop foreman works for years on the ideas of a great inventor, makes working models that may be tried and checked. Now by great inventor I don't mean one of the erratic mathematical geniuses that research laboratories keep on their payroll to sober up when needed, but an engineer with a record of integrity and brilliant achievement. From his relations, the shop foreman learns to admire the man and his work. One day he comes on a plan of the inventor that doesn't seem right. It's out of character and apparently useless. Instead of condemning his patron as irresponsible and purposeless or perhaps denying the inventor's continued existence in his right mind, the shopman follows the plan through, and tries to puzzle out the baffling purpose."

Michael leaned back and continued.

"Now I feel this way about the inventor of the psycho-energic processes of life. I've never seen him but I've observed and checked a good deal of his work, and I've admired much of what I've seen as coming from a brilliant and purposeful mind that knows what it's about. As a result, when I see certain gross, self-centered men and women enjoying long, comfortable, prosperous lives and tasting much of the pleasure of the world while many humble, sensitive and often unselfish men and women pass on to their early graves with little visible reward, and when numerous children with unknown possibilities are buried before they have even a taste of life and its pleasure—then I say, this is not typical of the creative mind and integrity I've observed or of any creator high on spiritual levels. So to me this seeming injustice is one of the strongest bits of circumstantial evidence for the mistrust of apparent extinction."

"I don't get it," Carl said.

"I think Michael means," R. V. explained, "that if all people, good and bad, received their just or fair deserts in this life, he might be willing to concede that the Creator might let it go at that. But since this is plainly not so, he believes that a decent creator must have some concealed compensation."

"And you feel survival is such a compensation?" Carl asked.

"I'd rather say that the psycho-energic processes give us a glimpse of a much more brilliant plan—that when man enjoys contentment and pleasure, he stagnates, drawing on his established facilities and resources. But when he suffers, he establishes new expanded rates and energy flows for his greater facilities and resources which mean higher potential happiness and understanding. It's a blueprint that to me carries the mark of a noble and magnanimous inventor."

"I don't see why everybody doesn't believe in survival," Mohammed said.

"It's not so much belief as desire," Michael told him. "There are men who don't want survival at any price. Some were born with energy flows of such a sluggish nature that except for times of stimulation, life has been a burden, and to go on living more or less forever strikes them as monstrous. Others are tired, disillusioned, discouraged and want nothing so much as rest. Still others have taken such secret or open courses in life that the thought of survival of their enemies and those they wronged as well as the presence of unseen witnesses to all their secret acts is unthinkable. Then there's the strong ego to whom, especially in health, strength and youth, the prospect of oblivion releases, by virtue of its greater shock, more energy than the prospect of survival. This makes the prospect of oblivion to them more stimulating and desirable. Also, many men are pretty well of the flesh. They see, feel or recognize little that's higher. They listen to the fleshly brain which tells the truth when it declares that itself and its body must certainly die. In addition to these, there are some, especially moderns and scientists, who feel it's less credulous and superstitious, more worldly wise and realistic, to disbelieve, at least publicly, in life after death. Finally there's a class of sincere open-minded men who have no objection to survival if and when they're convinced of its truth. So far they see no proof, are convinced that when a man dies, that's the end of him except for what work and memories he leaves behind."

"That's the way I feel," Carl said.

"Yes," Michael smiled. "Most men disliking survival for other reasons believe they belong to the last named class."

"But you want survival for yourself, don't you, Michael?" Mohammed asked.

"I'm not entirely sure," Michael confessed. "I know I shall never be given the opportunity, but just the same I should first like to examine the conditions of survival. We long so much at times for a better existence that we don't always stop to think how little we actually know what it's going to be like. We know what life is like here and the suffering some of us go through when handicapped by serious energy deficiencies. But we always have the last-stand prospect of escape by death into a possible happier life or oblivion. Once this possibility is taken away, our last bridge will be burned behind us. Will we regret it? I don't know and must leave it to the broader wisdom and resources of the Great Inventor. Whatever is we'll have to take because that's the nature of things as they are."

"Either way, death looks pretty terrible," Milt said.

Michael looked at him, then at us, earnestly.

"I'm sure you can see that if we actually survive unhurt, perhaps even with greater well-being in a more energy-free existence, death and evil are both an illusion, and that nothing has happened except to our expanded rates and energy flows. The survivor of death must be something like the man who survives adversity or a serious operation and finds himself no worse and perhaps bettered by his experience."

"I can see it intellectually," R. V. said. "But it isn't so easy to feel it without the actual experience."

"Not only you," Michael told him with feeling. "Nearly always I find it very hard. For instance, some of our Mexican villages never see a doctor. When I look with my own eyes at what some poor victim goes through, my convictions sometimes turn to water, especially if it's a woman or child. Their suffering may be for their eventual benefit psycho-energically, but I'm not satisfied with that. I can only think of their tragedy in human terms, and pray for their relief from the wheel of fate."

He stopped.

"Go on, Michael," R. V. urged. "Tell us what you pray."

Michael looked as if he had already said too much.

"I don't know if I do right or not." He spoke very low. "I pray for a milder and gentler evolutionary system, for a good means to a good end. I know and admit the effectiveness of E C E. I know that left alone, man fails to advance on his own, takes the easiest way, loves pleasure and stagnation. But try him again, I ask. Give him another chance and he'll struggle up to understanding. He'll do it slowly perhaps, slip back at times, but eventually he'll make it. Eternity must have a great deal of time. I acknowledge the Creator's high ambition for us and His brilliant processes in our behalf, but couldn't some of us linger longer on the way and enjoy the stages of growth we've won?"

He didn't look at us this time. We kept very quiet.

"Do you have any other personal prayer, Michael?" R. V. asked.

He was silent for a little.

"Many," he answered. "One I'd like to mention in the hope you may use it, too. It's my most common prayer. I pray for those in despair. Please think of and pray for them. It takes only a moment and may be done many times during the day."

"How do you do it?" Mohammed asked.

"Just think of those over the world in despair and have pity on them," Michael said. "Your prayer will come of itself. If you want to, you can add something more. I've spoken of the mysterious inner balance of energy that comes to us sometimes. It seems to hold an energy surplus that dissolves every fear and pain. The possessor of this boon while it lasts has security against every form of evil. You might pray that those in despair may know this evil-dissolving peace at the end. Then death and its bitterness would mean nothing. They could slip from life unencumbered and free."

"A while ago you questioned your right to pray this," R. V. said. "Why did you do that?"

"If death's the end, then I have no doubt. But should there be actual and very generous survival, I may be only interfering with the universe and the timing of processes arranged for our benefit. For example, the happy death I pray for provides no E C E process. Survival then turns out to be just an extension of happy peaceful living. No higher expenditure is established for energy release. On the other hand, dying in pain, despair and expectation of bitter extinction and then awaking to the reality of survival in a desirable state would provide a release of pain-energy so powerful that it should light up the surviving instrument almost with incandescence. It would seem a miracle and our sense of relief and joy and perhaps gratitude should give us a great upsurge of power in such a new life."

We were sobered.

"If we survive, what in us survives?" Dennis asked.

Michael considered.

"None of us actually knows," he said. "But we can speculate that the surviving instrument should get the benefit of our increased capabilities provided by the E C E process. Otherwise, there would be no point or purpose in it. We don't know of what substance this surviving instrument may be made or what manner of refined energy it uses. We do know that we actually have such a psycho-energic instrument in us so long as we're alive. As we all realize, it's just about the most extraordinary, even preposterous instrument in existence. It's capable, according to its varying inheritance and experience, of endless, sensitive, intelligent and extremely complex shades of response, sensation, perception and R process sequences to the universe and life. We call it the mind, sometimes the heart, sometimes the senses, sometimes the emotions or intuition. For all we know, part of the instrument that serves us during life may be what survives. If there's a dual instrument, the surviving part to make sense should undergo the same expansion, contraction and broadening of energy expenditure in life as the fleshly instrument."

R. V. was leaning forward.

"Tell us something about the surviving instrument."
Michael's eyes searched his face.

"I can't tell you much. It's guarded from me as from everyone else." He hesitated and rose. "Could we take a little ride? It might be the last we all have together."

When we went to our cars, Michael asked if we could drive up the mountain. Down at lower altitudes, we could see that the weather had cleared. In the Estancia Valley the sun was shining. Here it had stopped raining but heavy clouds still hung over the mountain, hiding its bulk above eight thousand feet. We would be able to see nothing up there. The forestry road would be muddy and there were sheer drops from the road's edge. But if Michael wanted to go, we said we'd take him.

On Sunday afternoons as a rule, cars from Albuquerque bring picnickers to the mountain and visitors to the top. Today after the rain we passed only two cars coming down, one at the mouth of Sulphur Canyon and one at Tree Spring. When finally we reached the crest, we found it deserted. For the last few miles a thick white mist had closed us in. We were literally in the clouds.

Michael waited until we were out of our cars.

"You asked me to give you some description of a possible surviving self in us," he reminded. "You saw the two cars that passed us? What description can you give me of the drivers?"

We looked at each other and said nothing.

"You certainly saw the cars," Michael persisted. "What did you see?"

We consulted. All we could tell him was that one car was green, we thought, the other black; that one was a pickup truck with a water bag hanging from the radiator, and that one of the drivers wore glasses.

"Is that all?" Michael asked, and when we nodded, "Well, that's about as much as we know about the real man or surviving instrument inside of us. What we mostly see and judge by are the material appearance and qualities of the carrying car. The driver himself, if there is one as I suspect, is so concealed and blended with the personality of his car that so long as the man is in the car it's very difficult to tell where the car stops and the driver begins."

"Why can't we tell the quality of a man's surviving instrument by the way he acts?"

"Because the way he acts and thinks may not be due to the surviving instrument. We know that the mechanically advanced and perfected car gives the driver an appearance of power, speed, brilliance and performance. But the manufacturer is responsible for it, not the driver. In an automobile race, you can't distinguish the philosopher from the professional except to look for the philosopher to finish in the rear rather than out in front."

"You think there's as much difference in surviving instruments as in men?"

"I should think a great deal more. The creative mind of the universe must be so far advanced over that of man that man can't conceive of him. On the other hand, intelligent man isn't at all far advanced over ignorant man. You can take an ignorant boy and make quite an intelligent man out of him in a relatively few years."

We watched him.

"If there's so much difference in surviving instruments, shouldn't there be some sign of whether a person has a high or low instrument?" Mohammed persisted.

"We can speculate, of course, but signs could only be assumption or suspicion," Michael answered. "First we have no scientific proof as yet of the existence of what you want me to valuate. Secondly, even if we did, we'd have difficulty separating its qualities from those of physical inheritance. Certain family strains have built up the higher qualities of intelligence, integrity, decency and even a kind of spirituality in their progeny. Now if a man with such qualities had ancestors with the same qualities, it would be very difficult to tell whether such traits were due to his blood inheritance or to an advanced surviving instrument. It might be either or both."

"What if a man has qualities he doesn't have in his ancestors?"

"Then I should be more disposed to talk about a non-physical cause," Michael said. "But I wouldn't think it a sure or essential requirement."

"How do you know higher characteristics relate to the spiritual?" Carl asked.

"Well, the more advanced a human being is generally considered by man, the more his energy flows appear connected not so much to pleasures of the animal world as to things of what we roughly call the spirit. On the other hand, men of animal natures have little energy flows attached to things of the spirit, which they find tame and dull. Of course, the development is never even. The same individual may have a combination of both."

"What about the man who shows no qualities of the spirit at all?" Mohammed asked. "He must have a very low-grade surviving instrument."

"Not necessarily. We know that a superior man is made to appear inferior and even foolish driving a crippled and mechanically imperfect car. So it's quite possible that an inferior and imperfect physical machine may hold a surviving instrument of superior quality whose advanced psycho-energic scale is helpless to express itself. Its multiple, sensitive R process sequences would be limited by the imperfect reactions of the physical and mental machine."

"Don't you consider that evil?" Carl asked. "I mean imprisoning a superior self in an inferior body and mind?"

"The E C E process, however long and painful, isn't necessarily evil," Michael insisted. "You remember how imprisonment sets up higher expanded rates and flows in the moth so that it soars when released. Also it was the E C E processes that established energy flows in the crippled legs of the lame man in the Bible so that when cured, he leaped for joy. Well, so, I imagine, would a superior surviving instrument leap to find itself finally freed from imprisonment in an inferior body and mind."

"What about the inferior surviving instrument in a superior body?" Milt asked. "How would he feel?"

"The driver of a high-powered car doesn't usually consider himself inferior," Michael pointed out. "The superiority of the car gives him a feeling of power and ability. In fact, he may not be aware that he's an inferior driver until he wrecks the car and is separated from it. That's also the time when the inferior surviving instrument would discover its inferiority."

"Isn't that a pretty cruel trick to play on man?" Carl asked. "Make him think he's higher than he is and then expose him?"

"I don't think so," Michael said earnestly. "Most inferior men love to drive superior cars. In the case of an inferior surviving instrument, it would have for a time at least the educational benefit of a superior intelligence and set of feelings."

"If I suspected I wasn't all I had been given reason to believe I was, I'd be pretty resentful toward God," Carl said.

"You might," Michael agreed, "but your resentment would only add another E C E process for your eventual benefit. Meantime your conjectures should give you warmer feelings toward all men. If your neighbor was arrogant and superior, the possibility that he might in reality be an inferior surviving instrument with very much farther to go evolutionarily than you should claim your potential pity for him. On the other hand, if he seemed low and inferior, the possibility that he nevertheless might have a higher surviving instrument than you should increase your potential respect for him. Also, if you suspected your own surviving instrument to be inferior to your racial intelligence, you might want to make some use of it's superiority while you were fortunate enough to have it."

"How could you do that?"

"You might use its intelligence to instruct your ignorant surviving self with some of the psycho-energic facts of life and death, so it wouldn't be left quite so naked, bewildered and confused when separated from its more advanced body."

When he finished talking, Michael led the way up the rocky crest. We were on the top of the mountain, nearly eleven thousand feet above sea level. We might as well have been shut up in an ivory tower. A veil of heavy white vapor closed us in. Clouds kept rolling up from below, constantly surrounding us.

"We can see nothing," Michael told us wryly, "or at least nothing beyond twenty or thirty yards. And yet we have reason to believe that spread out just a mile below us is a very real and immense tableland, a golden tableland with the sun shining on it at this moment and blue sky above it. What would a coney born and raised in the mist of the mountain think of us? He'd think us very foolish for such a fantastic idea."

He looked around at the rocks to get his bearings, then thrust out his arm.

"But human beings are very stubborn in their convictions. For instance, ten or fifteen miles in that direction I have reason to believe are Albuquerque and the Rio Grande. Sixty or seventy miles farther to the west should be Mount Taylor. Behind us should be the hills of Pedernal and a hundred miles or so to the southwest the Magdalenas and the Datils. I'm even fatuous enough to believe that if this veil of clouds was torn away, we could actually see all these mountains at such fabulous distances."

None of us said anything. We watched him closely as he bent forward, trying to peer through the misty stuff.

"I thought for a moment I caught a glimpse of something, but no, I can see nothing. And yet in my mind I think I can see the country bounded by these mountains and hills very clearly. I've often asked myself, why do we feel about our Southwestern country as we do? On first being exiled here, we may fiercely dislike it. Let us stay a while and we can scarcely bear to leave it. Away from it, we seldom fail to remember it without longing."

We had no answer. He went on.

"Is it our greater hours of sunshine, the increased metabolism of higher altitudes or could it be that the essence of a still higher life and its beings comes down to us purer and stronger in this rarer, less earthy air? Certainly I never felt the golden power of my devotions in the tropics or at ordinary altitudes as I do here where, according to this notion, the essence of higher things may fall on us like cosmic rays from outer space."

He moved over to take the arm of R. V., who was standing with the statue-like erectness of the blind at the edge of the great precipice where a false step might mean disaster. Michael continued.

"I mention these things for what they may be worth. There's something else, something closer, I think, to the truth. I mean the E C E of the desert. Could that be the secret of our greater power and well-being here, and why shouldn't we have thought of it sooner? What is the desert with its rugged and barren spaces, with its lack of rain for crops and thirst, but the land of hardship and expanded expenditure? And yet miraculously on our desert we have water, food, shelter and comfort, dissolving the painful expenditure and releasing its energy to make our oasis the most goodly place we know."

While he talked, I thought it had grown brighter, that the mist had thinned a little. Suddenly as often happens on a mountain peak, a change in the wind shifted the clouds. For a moment we could look through a vapory window on a wide, brilliant and sunlit world stretching endlessly under an incredibly blue sky. Far to the west we had a glimpse of Mount Taylor covered with clouds and bathed in blue light. Still farther to the southwest the white-capped Magdalenas and Datils stood revealed on the violet horizon, while at our backs we could see the Hills of Pedernal cloudless and fire-red in the late rays of the sun. Everywhere in between lay the desert country, bright, golden and threaded by uncounted lacy networks of arroyos.

As silently as the clouds parted, they closed over us

again, rolling up from below in fleecy white billows and along the mountain crest. In a few moments we could see nothing, not even our cars.

"Did we see it or didn't we?" Michael mused. "Was it real or only an illusion, a trick of the brain? Do these places we thought we saw actually exist? Can we definitely prove it without going there? Or must we decide on what evidence we have, each for himself according to his individual inheritance and experience?"

A NOTE ON THE TYPE

The text of this book was set on the Linotype in JANSON, a recutting made direct from the type cast from matrices made by Anton Janson. Whether or not Janson was of Dutch ancestry is not known, but it is known that he purchased a foundry and was a practicing type-founder in Leipzig during the years 1660 to 1687. Janson's first specimen sheet was issued in 1675. His successor issued a specimen sheet showing all of the Janson types in 1689.

His type is an excellent example of the influential and sturdy Dutch types that prevailed in England prior to the development by William Caslon of his own incomparable designs, which he evolved from these Dutch faces. The Dutch in their turn had been influenced by Garamond in France. The general tone of Janson, however, is darker than Garamond and has a sturdiness and substance quite different from its predecessors. It is a highly legible type, and its individual letters have a pleasing variety of design. Its heavy and light strokes make it sharp and clear, and the full-page effect is characterful and harmonious.

This book was composed, printed, and bound by THE PLIMPTON PRESS, Norwood, Massachusetts. Paper manufactured by S. D. WARREN COMPANY, Boston. Typography and binding designs are by W. A. DWIGGINS.